Shape

impact

MATHS HOMEWORK

Published by Scholastic Publications Ltd,
Villiers House,
Clarendon Avenue,
Leamington Spa,
Warwickshire CV32 5PR

© 1994 Scholastic Publications Ltd
Text © 1994 University of North
London Enterprises Ltd

UNIVERSITY OF
NORTH LONDON

Activities by the IMPACT Project
at the University of North
London, collated and rewritten
by Ruth Merttens and Ros Leather

Editor Jo Saxelby-Jennings
Assistant editor Joanne Boden
Designer Tracey Ramsey
Series designer Anna Oliwa
Illustrations Clinton Banbury Design Associates
Cover illustration Anna Oliwa

Designed using Aldus Pagemaker
Processed by Pages Bureau, Leamington Spa
Artwork by Pages Bureau, Leamington Spa
Printed in Great Britain by Clays Ltd,
Bungay, Suffolk

British Library Cataloguing-in-Publication Data
A catalogue record for this book is
available from the British Library.

ISBN 0-590-53332-0

Shape

impact
CONTENTS

Shape

impact
CONTENTS

impact
INTRODUCTION

This series of IMPACT books is designed to help you run a non-traditional homework scheme. Through the use of take-home maths activities, children can share maths with a parent/carer in the context of the home. The results of these activities then feed back into the classwork at school.

IMPACT works through the following processes:
● Teachers plan their maths for the next few weeks as usual and consider which parts might usefully be done at home.
● Teachers look through selected activities which fit in with what they are planning.
● The activities are photocopied and sent home with the children every week or fortnight.
● The results of each activity are brought back into the classroom by the children and form part of the following week's classwork.

In practice this process will be slightly different in each classroom and in each school. Teachers may adapt it to fit their own way of working and the ethos of the school in which they work. Most schools send out IMPACT activities fortnightly, although some do send it weekly. There is some evidence to suggest that weekly activities get a slightly better response and help to raise standards more effectively than fortnightly, but this is not conclusive. The important point is that each teacher should feel comfortable with how often the IMPACT activities are used in his/her class.

Planning

When you, the teacher, are looking at your work and deciding what maths, roughly speaking, you plan to be doing over the next few weeks, all that is necessary is to consider which parts may usefully be done or practised at home. It is helpful if, over a period of time, a range of activities are chosen in order to vary the mathematical experience in the home and the type and amount of follow-up required in class.

The activities tend to fall into three broad categories:
● Activities which practise a skill – these can be followed up in the routine classwork the children are doing. They must be carefully selected by the teacher according to the level of the children.
● Activities which collect data – these lead into work on data handling and representation.
● Activities in which children measure or make something – this produces an object or some measurements to be used later in class.

The activities in this book are divided into four sections according to age: Year 3, Year 4, Year 5 and Year 6. There are two pages of teachers' notes relating to the individual activities at the beginning of each section. All the activities are covered by the National Curriculum Attainment Target 'Shape, space and measures'. In general, the level of the activities is appropriate to the year of the child. Thus, Level 3 for Years 3 and 4 and Level 4 for Years 5 and 6. Since the activities will be done by a child with an adult, in the context of the home, they are slightly more demanding in terms of level than would normally be the case for shape activities in the classroom. Details of the relationships of the national curricula in Britain are given on page 96.

Working with parents

It is important for the success of IMPACT that the activities taken home are seen by the parents to be maths. We always suggest, at least until IMPACT is up and running and parents' confidence in it is well established, that activities are chosen which have a clearly mathematical purpose. Save the more 'wacky' activities until later! You will get a much better response if parents believe that what they are doing is maths.

Each activity contains a note to parents which explains the purpose of the activity and how they can best help. It also gives a reference to the attainment targets – although not to any level. Teachers who prefer not to have this can white it out. The IMPACT activities should be accompanied by an IMPACT diary, enabling parents and children to make their comments. See page 96 for details.

Making the most of IMPACT

The quickest way to reduce the number of children who share the maths at home is to ignore or be negative about the work they bring back into school. When the children come running into class, tripping over the string which went twice round their cat, it is difficult to welcome them all individually, but it is crucial that the activities are followed up in classwork. The nature and type of this follow-up depends very much upon the nature of the activity, and specific suggestions are made in the teachers' notes. However, some general points apply:
● Number activities, such as games, can often be repeated in a more formalised way in the classwork. For example, if the children have been playing a dice game, throwing two dice and adding the totals, they can continue to do this in the classroom, but this time they can record all the 'sums' in their maths book. This applies to any skills-practice activity.
● Data-collecting activities, of any description, need to be followed up by allowing the children to work together in small groups to collate, analyse and represent their joint data. This will inevitably involve discussion as to how the data was obtained and any problems encountered while obtaining it.
● If the children have made or measured something at home, the information or the object needs to be used as part of the resulting classwork. This will not be too difficult since this type of activity is selected by the teacher precisely in order to provide the measurements or shapes for use in class.

The implication of this is that it is wise to select a variety of activities to send home. No teacher wants to drown in data, nor do they want all the IMPACT activities to result in more routine number work. Some activities generate lots of follow-up work while others require minimal follow-up – perhaps just a discussion about who won or lost, and how many times they played the game.

Many of the activities can lead to an attractive display or enable the teacher to make a class book. Such a book does not have to be 'grand'. It can be simply five or six large sheets of sugar paper folded in the middle and stitched/stapled with the children's work mounted inside it. The children love these books, and they make a fine record of their work. An IMPACT display board in the school entrance hall gives parents a sense that their work at home is appreciated.

For further details of IMPACT see page 96.

Teachers' notes
YEAR THREE

Reflect your name The children may enjoy the story 'The dog and the bone' in *Aesop's Fables* (Usborne) or *The Rain Puddle* by Adelaide Hall (Bodley Head) *(out of print – try local libraries)* or one of the traditional tales about catching the moon in a puddle – all on the theme of reflection. Can the children write messages using only reflected letters? How quickly can their messages be read by others? Can the children reflect their phone numbers? Are any numbers the same upside-down as the right way up (0 or 1, for example)?

Which box? Some of the children could make three-dimensional shapes from Polydron or a similar construction kit and then be encouraged to write precise instructions describing how their models were made for others to attempt to follow. Amendments could be made to the instructions, if necessary.

Which face? The children could choose classroom boxes to measure, recording their measurements carefully. Ask questions such as, 'What is the difference between the long side and the short side of each oblong in your box? Which face has the smallest or largest difference? Are there any faces without a difference?'

Quadrilateral Lotto The children may like to make large quadrilaterals to hang on a 'washing line'. Play this game – one child describes a shape on the line geometrically, then another tries to guess which one it is. You may like to introduce geometrical vocabulary such as 'trapezium' and 'kite'. Talk about which shapes are the same if you turn them upside-down – squares, oblongs and the rhombus. Discuss which shapes have right angles in them. Which shapes have no right angles?

Cuboid sort-out Using Polydron or a similar construction kit the children could make large numbers of cuboids. Can they sort them into families? How many types of cuboids are there? Is it possible to make a cuboid with square and oblong faces? Help the children to construct the net of a cuboid. What arrangements of six rectangles will fold up to create a cuboid?

Dice drawing The children could discuss how many right angles they have discovered. How many right angles should there be on a dice? Is it the same for all cuboids? The children could investigate using different sizes and shapes of cuboid. Make a four-sided dice using a tetrahedron (a net is provided on page 92 of this book). How many right-angles does this have? What about a square-based pyramid?

Angle search The children may like to sort their drawings into those that are exactly 90°, those that are smaller than 90° and those that are larger than 90°. These can be displayed and questions asked, such as, 'Which are the smallest and largest angles? Estimate how many degrees there are in these angles? How can we find

out each of the angles?' Produce templates of 45°, 30° and 60°. Let the children use these to help them to estimate the size of different angles. Introduce the names of angles bigger than 90°, but smaller than 180° (obtuse) and smaller than 90° (acute).

Cuboid symmetry Put all the half boxes in a pile. If each child takes one half of a box, how quickly can they find the child with the other half of the same box? Can the children arrange themselves into three sets: 'vertical symmetry', 'horizontal symmetry' and 'diagonal symmetry'? Make other shapes to cut in half; for example, a tetrahedron (a net is provided on page 92 of this book). Can this be cut exactly in half so as to produce two identical pieces? Talk about its line of symmetry.

Cylinder symmetry How many different ways are there of cutting a cylinder so that the halves are symmetrical? Can they be grouped using the vocabulary 'vertical symmetry', 'horizontal symmetry' and 'diagonal symmetry'? Perhaps a mirror could be used to check for symmetry. Make a cone. Does this have a line of symmetry? Is it symmetrical about a horizontal line or a vertical line?

Clock angles Working in groups, the children may be able to arrange the clocks showing 90° angles in a pattern; for example, 3 o'clock, five past 4, ten past 5 and so on. Display these clocks with the appropriate times written underneath. Extend this activity by finding the times when there is an angle of less than 90° between the hands and those when there is an angle of more than 90°. Is there a pattern?

Four-triangle shapes The children could work systematically to make all the possible combinations of four triangles. These could be displayed using different types of classification. The next 'large' triangle is composed of nine smaller triangles. What is the one after that? What numbers of small triangles will fit together to make large triangles (4, 9, 16...)? Can the children see a pattern in these numbers?

Street patterns If you have a Valiant Roamer or Turtle in school, the children could design a street pattern for it to follow. They could draw simple maps of the classroom (or whole school) and write instructions for routes to various areas of the room (or school), which could be used with

the Roamer or Turtle also. Alternatively, let the children produce a series of instructions for a small space alien who lands in his space buggy and needs to be 'programmed' to get around!

Weather vane A group of children could design and make a weather vane. This could be used to collect information about wind direction. The wind direction could be shown on a large map of Europe. Discuss why we prefer winds from certain directions. Talk about the compass directions: north, east, south and west. How do the children remember the order of these round the compass? Try 'Never Eat Shredded Wheat' or 'west–east spells we'.

Design a weather vane The children will need to be given time to demonstrate how their designs work. They could design a chart to collect information about wind direction over a period of time. Discuss how the children are going to remember the order of the points of a compass ('Never Eat Shredded Wheat') and talk about the intermediate points – SW, NE and so on. Draw a large class compass with all these intermediate points marked.

Bedroom to scale The children could begin to find the areas of different shapes in their bedrooms by counting the squares. Who has a bed, wardrobe or toy box of the smallest or largest area? The children may like to find the area of regular shapes in the classroom using squared paper. The bedroom pictures could be displayed in a class book.

Symmetrical patterns How many patterns have only one line of symmetry? Are there any patterns that are vertically,

horizontally *and* diagonally symmetrical. Use isometric (triangular) paper (provided on page 95 of this book) and a pattern book to encourage the children to create complicated symmetrical patterns. Discuss snowflake patterns. These are all based on the hexagon. Using the isometric paper, create hexagonal patterns which have at least two lines of symmetry.

Frog symmetry Display the symmetrical pictures and attempt to categorise them. The children may like to extend their ideas by folding the paper into quarters and drawing patterns that have two planes of symmetry. Use a creature other than a frog – such as a turtle. Can this be drawn so as to be vertically and horizontally symmetrical?

Find the treasure The children should be encouraged to write programs for the Valiant Roamer or Turtle which will create pathways round objects in the classroom. It may be helpful if the children walk their patterns before attempting to write the program. If you have no Roamer or Turtle, let the children produce a series of instructions for a small space alien who lands in his space buggy and needs to be 'programmed' to get around!

Three views The children may like to sort their shapes into those that have three different views, those that have two and those that are the same from all angles. Which shapes are the same from all angles (for example, a cube and a tetrahedron)? Which shapes are the same from two angles (for example, a cuboid and a square-based pyramid)? What about a sphere?

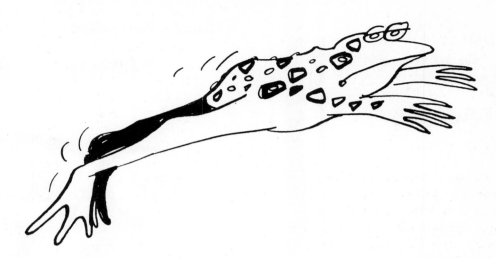

How many squares? The children may like to use overlapping coloured tissue paper squares of differing sizes to create other patterns. If these are displayed against a window, the squares will become more visible and attractive. Can the children create a similar puzzle using another shape, such as triangles? What about rectangles (which include oblongs and squares!)?

Jigsaw squares The children could display their shapes. They may like to use some similar shapes to create oblongs. How many different oblongs can be produced? Can they make a triangular jigsaw? What about a hexagonal one? Talk about which shapes would be difficult – such as circles.

Walk a letter The children could work in small groups, using the Roamer or Turtle, to check their results. Also, instructions for the different letters could be read out in PE. All the children could face in the same

direction before beginning and walking the letter together. Can the children also walk a number? Which numbers are difficult? Which are easy? What about two-digit numbers?

Jigsaw shapes It will be necessary to allow the children to discuss their jigsaws and to try out each others' ideas. What makes a good jigsaw? Can some ideas be improved or refined? Care must be taken to value all contributions. The children can be encouraged to create jigsaws to specific criteria – for example, one where all the pieces are triangular, or all the pieces are pentagons.

Worms The children may like to plot their patterns on the computer. They could use a program such as the LOGO-type *Arrow* (Nimbus) (Abingdon: Flexible Software Ltd., PO Box 100, Abingdon, Oxon., OX16 6PQ). These patterns could be printed and displayed with written instructions alongside.

Dear Parent or Carer

Help may be required
to ensure that the
letters are as large
and as bold as
possible. Please
remind your child
that the letters must
rest on the line above
the fold. Care must
be taken when
cutting them out.

National Curriculum
reference:
Maths Attainment Target
**Shape, space and
measures**

_____and

child

_____

helper(s)

_____

did this activity together

Reflect your name

YOU WILL NEED a sheet of paper folded in half.

● Draw a line about half a centimetre from the fold.

● Write your name in big letters, so that the edges of the letters touch the line.

● Cut out your name carefully – be sure NOT to cut along the fold line.

● Open out your name – what do you notice?

● Can you use a mirror to create the same effect with your name? Where do you need to hold the mirror?

impact MATHS HOMEWORK

Which box?

YOU WILL NEED: several boxes, tins or cartons from the cupboard.

● With your helper, measure all the boxes and discuss their shapes.

● Take turns to choose one of the boxes secretly.

● Your helper will need to ask questions to decide which box you have chosen. They may only ask questions about its shape and size. Good questions may be: 'Does it have six oblong faces?' or 'Is it taller than 25cm?'

Dear Parent or Carer

Your child may need reminding that the sides of boxes are called 'faces'. Please help your child to measure the boxes before you begin playing the game. Encourage your child to make notes about each box.

National Curriculum reference:
Maths Attainment Target
Shape, space and measures

_____and

child

_____

helper(s)

_____

did this activity together

Which face?

● Choose one box or carton from the cupboard.

● Carefully and secretly measure one face in every direction necessary.

● Stand the box on the table.

● Then your helper will need to ask suitable questions to find out which face you have chosen. They may ask questions about its shape and size only. A good question may be, 'Is the face an oblong?'

Quadrilateral Lotto

A game for three people – a caller and two players.

● Cut out the small shape cards below for the caller to use and a strip of shapes for each player.

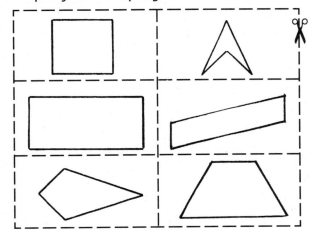

HOW TO PLAY:

● Without looking, the caller picks a shape card.

● The caller looks at the chosen shape card and then describes the shape on it to the other two players.

● The first player to point to that shape on their strip uses the shape card to cover it.

● Play until all the shape cards are gone. Who has covered the most shapes or is it a draw? Play again.

● Can you invent another similar game?

Dear Parent or Carer

Please encourage the caller to describe the shapes carefully using phrases such as, 'The four sides are the same length...; the four corners are all right angles (or 90° angles)....' It is sufficient at this stage to describe other angles as simply more than or less than 90°.

National Curriculum reference:
Maths Attainment Target
Shape, space and measures

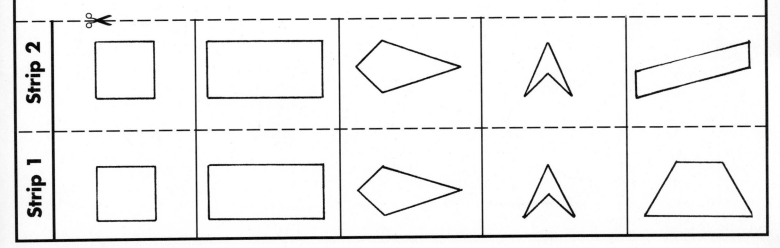

_____and

child

_____

helper(s)

_____

did this activity together

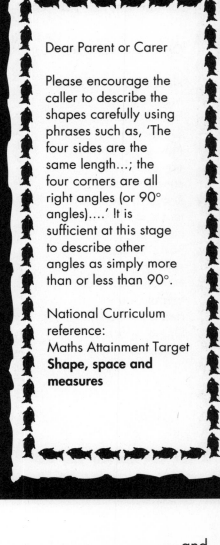

_____and
child

_____
helper(s)

_____
did this activity together

Cuboid sort-out

YOU WILL NEED: *a selection of boxes
and packets from the cupboard.*

● Draw the boxes in the correct sets.

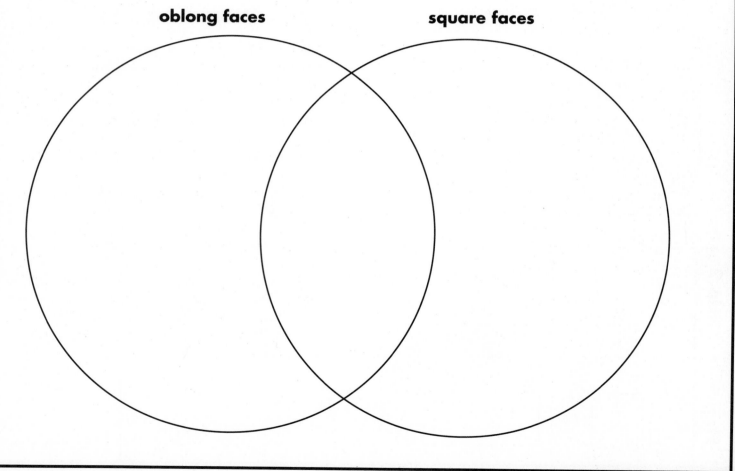

oblong faces   **square faces**

impact MATHS HOMEWORK

Dice drawing

I have drawn my dice so that I can see three of its faces:

1

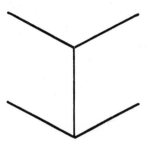

2

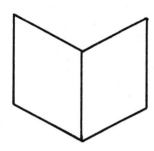

3

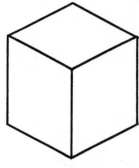

4

● Can you draw a dice to show the missing faces?

● What numbers will you be showing on your dice?

● How many 90° angles are there on an actual dice?

Dear Parent or Carer

Help may be required to draw the dice. Please encourage your child to practise drawing the shape.
Your child may like to make a right angle (90° angle) from two joined strips of paper to help with counting the 90° angles on the actual dice.

National Curriculum reference:
Maths Attainment Target
Shape, space and measures

_____and

child

_____

helper(s)

_____

did this activity together

impact MATHS HOMEWORK

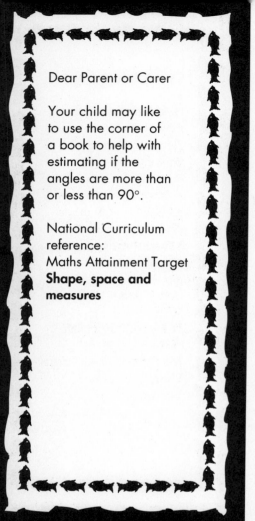
_____and

child

_____

helper(s)

_____

did this activity together

Angle search

This symbol ° means degrees.
All these angles are 90° (ninety degrees).

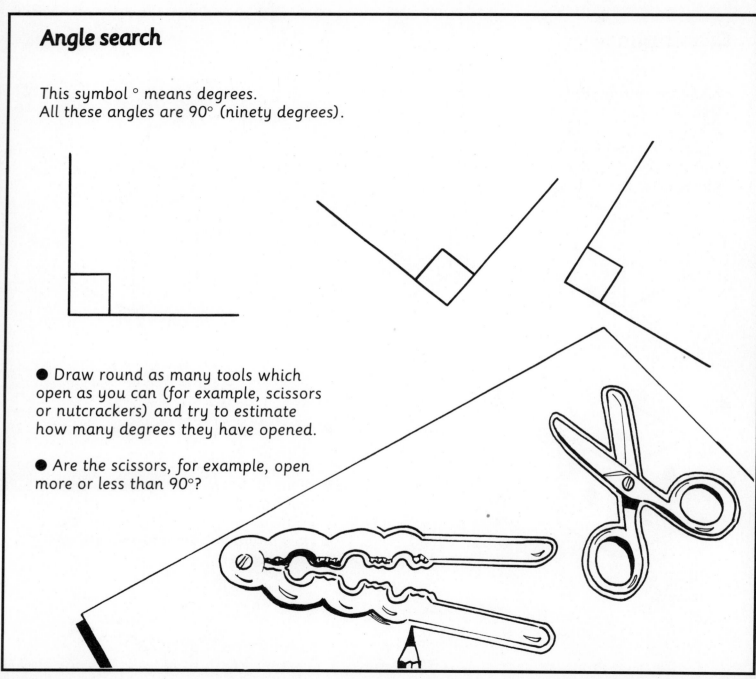

● Draw round as many tools which open as you can (for example, scissors or nutcrackers) and try to estimate how many degrees they have opened.

● Are the scissors, for example, open more or less than 90°?

impact MATHS HOMEWORK

Cuboid symmetry

- Find an empty box.

- Can you cut your box so that both halves are symmetrical? It may be helpful to draw a line before you begin to cut.

- Please bring the two halves of your box into school.

Dear Parent or Carer

Please encourage your child to discuss where the cut will be made. Is there only one way of cutting the box? Encourage your child to use the vocabulary 'vertical', 'horizontal' and 'diagonal'.

National Curriculum reference:
Maths Attainment Target
Shape, space and measures

_____and

child

_____

helper(s)

_____

did this activity together

impact MATHS HOMEWORK

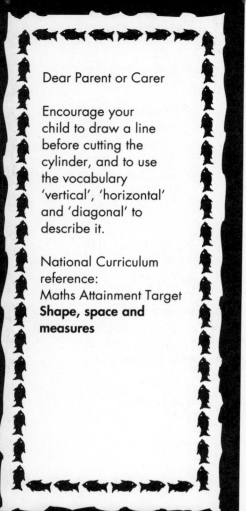

_____and

child

_____

helper(s)

_____

did this activity together

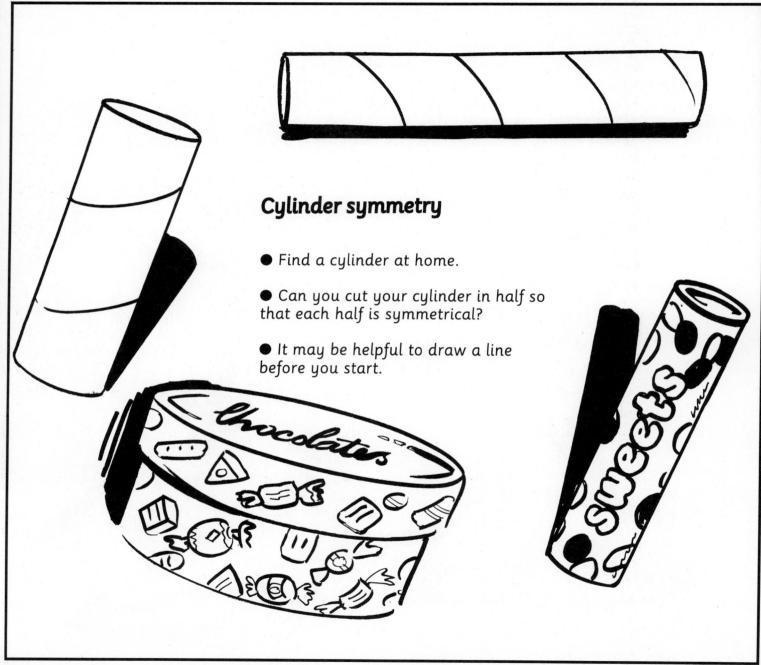

Cylinder symmetry

● Find a cylinder at home.

● Can you cut your cylinder in half so that each half is symmetrical?

● It may be helpful to draw a line before you start.

Clock angles

● Stick the clock face and its hands on to card (an old cereal box or the back of an old birthday card will do).

● Cut them out and attach the hands to the clock face using a split paper fastener to hold them in position.

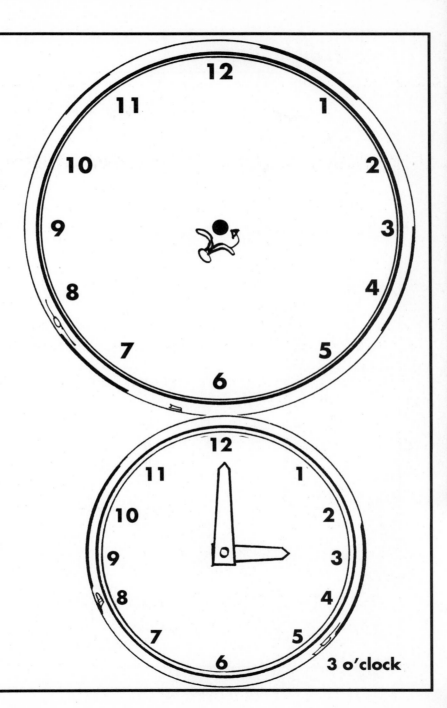

At 3 o'clock the distance between the hour and the minute hand is 90°.

● Can you find other clock times showing a 90° angle between the two hands and draw them?

● Bring some of your 90° times into school to share with other members of the class.

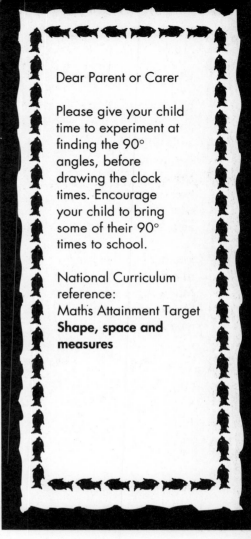

Dear Parent or Carer

Please give your child time to experiment at finding the 90° angles, before drawing the clock times. Encourage your child to bring some of their 90° times to school.

National Curriculum reference:
Maths Attainment Target
Shape, space and measures

_____and

child

_____

helper(s)

_____

did this activity together

_____and

child

_____

helper(s)

_____

did this activity together

Four-triangle shapes

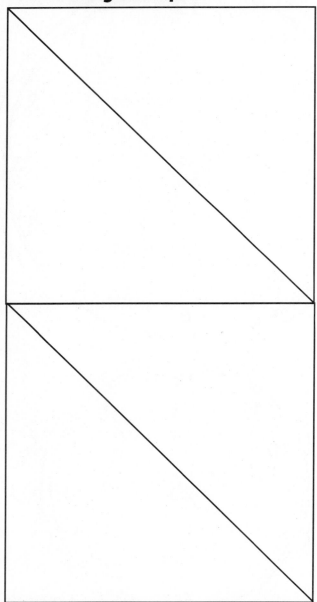

● Stick the two squares on to card (an old birthday card or cereal packet will do) and cut out the four triangles.

● How many different shapes can you make? (All the shapes must have edges that touch without an overlap.)

● Draw round the shape with the least number of vertices (corners) and the shape with the most vertices.

● Bring all your drawings to school.

Street patterns

Some new towns have street layouts that have been planned on a horizontal and vertical grid. The roads are named with an H for horizontal and a V for vertical. Each horizontal or vertical road has a number attached to it.

● If you arrived in this new town at the roundabout (V1, H7), how would you write instructions for reaching the church? Is yours the most direct route?

● Draw a garage at the junction of H4 and V3 and a school at (V2, H2).

● Can you plan a complicated journey to the church via the garage and the school? You could draw in some more buildings.

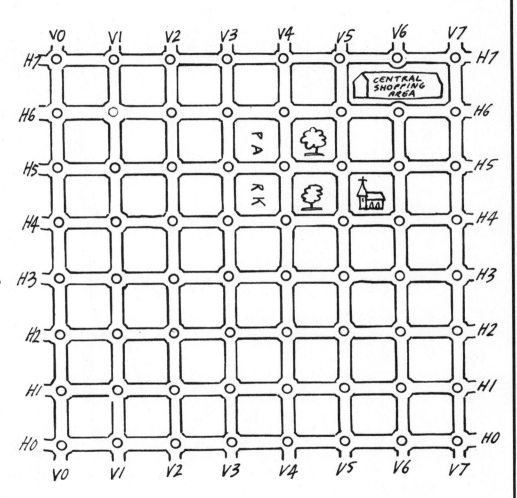

Dear Parent or Carer

Please encourage your child to write a sequence of instructions for each journey. For example: '1. Forwards through two roundabouts; 2. Left at the next roundabout....'

National Curriculum reference:
Maths Attainment Target
Shape, space and measures

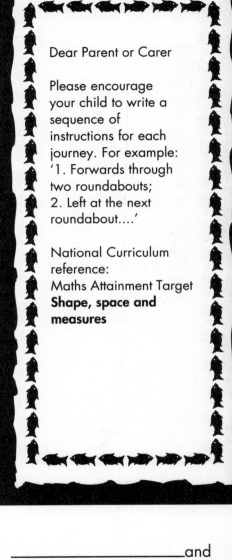

_____and

child

_____

helper(s)

_____

did this activity together

_____and

child

_____

helper(s)

did this activity together

Weather vane

● Is there a weather vane in your town? Can you draw it? Remember to write on any letters you can see.

● Which part of the weather vane turns and why?

● In which compass direction are you standing to draw your picture?

impact MATHS HOMEWORK

Design a weather vane

YOU WILL NEED: plenty of junk materials. (Yoghurt pots, empty boxes, some sticks or canes, some string and sticky tape may be useful for making your weather vane!)

● Ask someone at home to show you a weather vane in your town before you begin.

● Now work with your helper to design a weather vane.

Dear Parent or Carer

Please give your child time to suggest and try ideas – supported, suspended and so on. This model does not require hours in the tool shed! It would be an advantage if the work was carried out mainly by your child.

National Curriculum reference:
Maths Attainment Target
Shape, space and measures

_____and

child

_____

helper(s)

_____

did this activity together

_____and

child

_____

helper(s)

_____

did this activity together

Bedroom to scale

● You will need to imagine that you are looking down at your bedroom from above. What shapes can you see?

● Draw a scale picture of your bedroom on the 1cm squared paper.

impact MATHS HOMEWORK

Symmetrical patterns

● Complete and colour the picture on the grid so that it is symmetrical.

● Now design your own symmetrical picture on the grid.

● Use a mirror to find the lines of symmetry in both pictures.

● How many lines of symmetry are there?

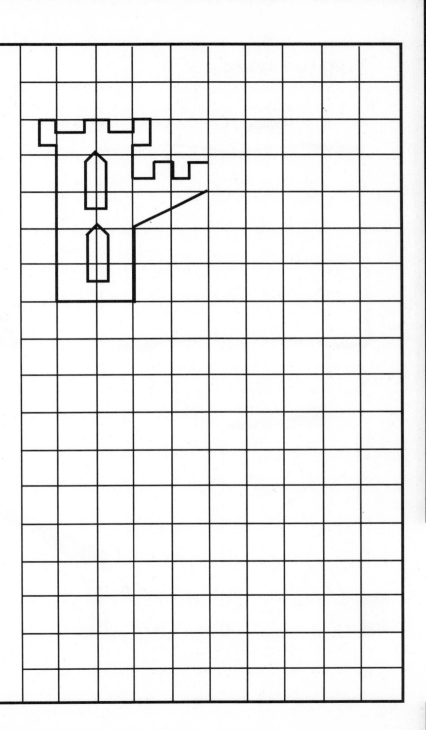

Dear Parent or Carer

Your child may need reminding that a pattern is only symmetrical if both halves match exactly.

National Curriculum reference:
Maths Attainment Target
Shape, space and measures

_____and

child

_____

helper(s)

_____

did this activity together

_____and

child

_____

helper(s)

_____

did this activity together

Frog symmetry

● Fold a piece of paper in half.

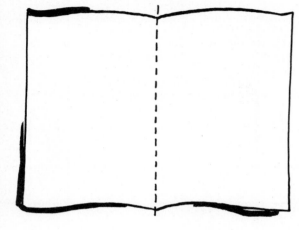

● Cut your picture out.

● Draw a picture on one half.

● What do you notice?

The folded line is called a 'line of
symmetry'.

● Create some symmetrical pictures
yourself – trees, flowers and people
make excellent symmetrical pictures.

impact MATHS HOMEWORK

Find the treasure

● Play this game with a friend.

● The 'instructor' secretly chooses a place in the room where the treasure is hidden. Then the 'explorer' must follow the instructions given to find the treasure.

● Instructions might be: 'Two steps forward turn clockwise 90°, then four steps forward and turn clockwise another 90°.'

● Take turns to play this game. Do your instructions improve?

Dear Parent or Carer

Your child may need to practise turning to the right for clockwise and to the left for anticlockwise. Please remember that 90° is a quarter turn.

National Curriculum reference:
Maths Attainment Target
Shape, space and measures

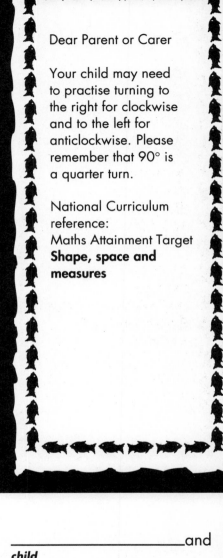

_____and

child

_____

helper(s)

_____

did this activity together

_____and

child

_____

helper(s)

_____

did this activity together

front view

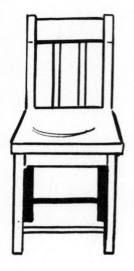

top view (looking down)

Three views

● Draw three views of a ball or a box or a cone or a cylinder or any other solid shapes that are in the home. You could use the back of this page.

side view

impact MATHS HOMEWORK

How many squares?

● How many squares do you think there are in this diagram?

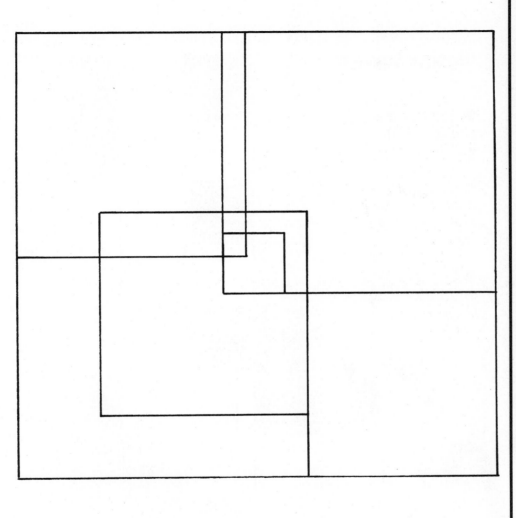

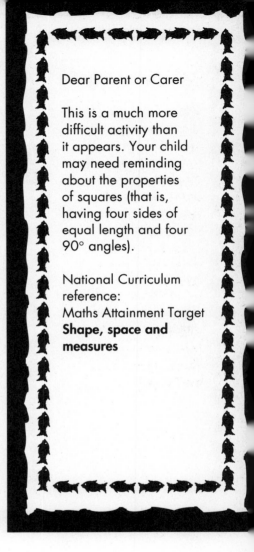

Dear Parent or Carer

This is a much more difficult activity than it appears. Your child may need reminding about the properties of squares (that is, having four sides of equal length and four 90° angles).

National Curriculum reference:
Maths Attainment Target
Shape, space and measures

_____and

child

_____

helper(s)

_____

did this activity together

_____and

child

_____

helper(s)

_____

did this activity together

Jigsaw squares

● Cut out the
shaded shapes
carefully.

● Can you re-
arrange them to
make two small
squares?

● Can you find
any other ways
to do this?

impact MATHS HOMEWORK

Walk a letter

● Write instructions for the Roamer or Turtle to write a particular letter.

● You will need to choose a letter that only has 90° turns in it. Each forward movement is 30cm. The Roamer and Turtle will only follow the instructions: forward, backwards, right turn and left turn.

For example, for a capital L:

> **Forward 1**
> **Right 90°**
> **Forward 2**

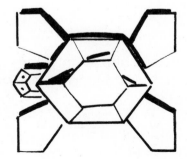

Dear Parent or Carer

Please help your child by walking to verbal instructions before attempting the writing. Valiant Roamers and Turtles are computer controlled machines used in schools for educational purposes. You may need to do this several times with different letters before beginning the task.

National Curriculum reference:
Maths Attainment Target
Shape, space and measures

_____and

child

_____

helper(s)

_____

did this activity together

_____and
child

_____
helper(s)

_____
did this activity together

Jigsaw shapes

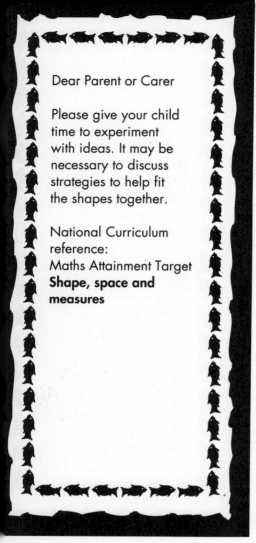

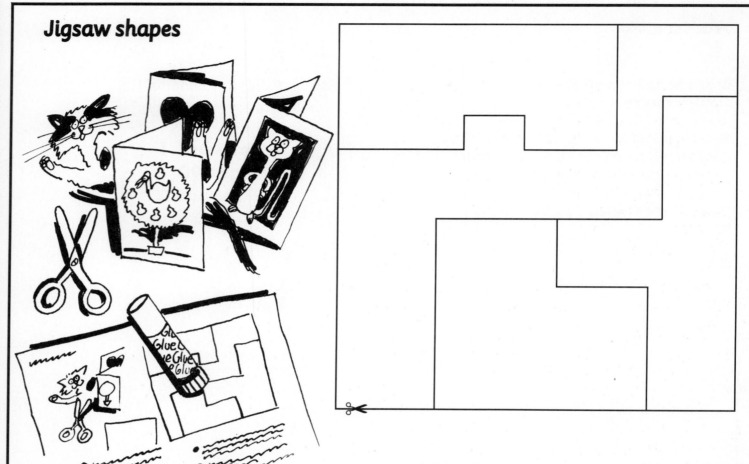

● Stick the pattern above on to an old birthday or Christmas card before cutting it out.

● Look at the design carefully – how quickly can you make the square again after shuffling the pieces?

● Design a shape jigsaw to bring back to school.

● You may like to begin with a circle or a square.

● Remember that it is important to keep a pattern of your jigsaw in case others have problems putting it together.

Worms

These particular worms can only turn through 90° in a clockwise direction. They perform a particular pattern which goes: 1 forward, turn; 2 forwards, turn; 3 forwards, turn; this pattern is then repeated.

● Can you draw the worm pattern on the dotted grid opposite?

● Using a different coloured pencil you may like to devise and draw a different worm pattern.

● Write instructions for your new worm pattern.

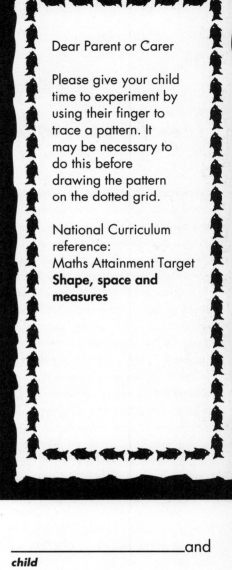

Dear Parent or Carer

Please give your child time to experiment by using their finger to trace a pattern. It may be necessary to do this before drawing the pattern on the dotted grid.

National Curriculum reference:
Maths Attainment Target
Shape, space and measures

_____and

child

_____

helper(s)

_____

did this activity together

Teachers' notes
YEAR FOUR

Compass UK As a follow-up to this activity, discuss visits in the UK that the children have made from home. Mark the various destinations on a large map. Each child could write down the directions for travelling to and returning from their visit. A chart could be made to show in which direction most children travelled. Discuss which places in the UK are generally agreed to be in the 'North'. Which places are in the 'South'? How do we describe Bristol, if we live in Exeter (the north-east!)?

A bird's-eye view of home Let the children group their homes using their chosen criteria. For example: all homes that have a garden facing south, all homes that have a front door facing east, all homes that have windows facing west and so on. These groups could be displayed around a large compass. When choosing criteria for sorting, remember to allow for those children whose homes may be flats or one room bedsits.

Church Traditionally, Church of England churches have the altar at the east end of a cruciform construction and the congregation sit down the east-west axis of the church, facing east. Have all the churches been drawn from the same direction?

Can the children guess from which direction other children were drawing their church? How many children were drawing from the north/south/east/west? The church pictures could be displayed with relevant directional information. Extend this activity to discuss other directions of religious significance. For example, explain that Muslims always face Mecca when they pray and that the wall in the mosque facing Mecca is called the 'qiblah' wall.

Triangular sandwiches The children may like to create a large triangular tessellation picture using quartered squares to show how the pattern grows. Does the pattern always tessellate? What other shape sandwiches can the children devise? What shapes are usual? Can they create triangular sandwiches with right-angled triangles? What shapes are biscuits? How about crackers? Which shapes tessellate?

Shadows By observation, can the children categorise their shadows in any way? How many children have shadows larger than themselves or shorter than themselves or the same length as themselves? Do the times when they were drawn suggest why this might be so? Select a child as a subject and draw and cut out his or her shadow from large sheets of paper at several times during the day. Indicate the time when each shadow was drawn. Display these shadow cut-outs with the times and the height of the child.

Circle symmetry The children could look at Islamic patterns and attempt to re-create the designs. They could try to find any lines of symmetry. This work could be displayed alongside their original patterns.

Extend the children's understanding of circles by drawing circles using a compass. Discuss how this is done, and talk about the radius of the circle. Can the children draw some concentric circles? What about overlapping circles? Some interesting patterns can be made with these.

Triangle letters The children can discuss the different types of triangle. Some have three acute angles (less than 90°), some have one right angle and some have an obtuse angle (more than 90°). Talk about these different types of angle – emphasise that the right angle is always used as the 'bench-mark' to recognise acute and obtuse angles. You can demonstrate that the three angles in a triangle add up to 180° (a straight line) by cutting out the three angles and laying them one beside another so that they make a straight line.

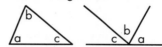

How far round? The children can compare the book or magazine perimeters. Whose book has the largest perimeter? Then they can calculate its area. Does it have the largest area? Can they calculate the areas of some other books? Does the book with the smallest area necessarily

have the smallest perimeter? Let the children try out different rectangles on squared paper. They could try several all with an area of 24 squares. What different perimeters can they get? For example, a rectangle with an area of 24 can have sides 1 × 24, or 2 × 12, or 3 × 8, or 4 × 6. Each of these will give very different perimeters. Then let them try a rectangle of area 36 squares. How many perimeters do they find with this? Then try a set perimeter – for example 40. What rectangles with different areas can be made?

Regular or not! The children can display their shape drawings. Which ones were hardest to draw? Is an oblong a regular quadrilateral? Why not? Can they draw a regular octagon? Is a circle regular? What other criteria for regularity might there be – for example, two lines of symmetry. This would make an oblong regular! What other shapes have two lines of symmetry – for example a 'house' shape (a pentagon). Can the children draw a pentagon with equal sides but without equal angles?

Vertical Please allow the children time to demonstrate the effectiveness of their designs. It may be possible to bring into school a plumb-line and a spirit-level to show the children. The children may like to use these to check the walls in school.

Can they check the tables using a spirit-level to see if they are horizontal? Discuss the right angles which occur where the horizontals meet the verticals. Find examples of these.

Reflecting squares How many different patterns have the children made? Are they all different? The children may like to investigate what happens when three squares, or shapes other than squares, are reflected. Let the children use isometric paper (provided on page 95 of this book) to draw hexagons. Can the children create hexagonal reflecting patterns? Do any of their patterns have two lines of symmetry? Look at the rotational symmetry in their patterns as well.

Straws The children may like to investigate the least number of straws needed for making one, two, three, four triangles and so on. Then these could be made with straws and displayed. The children may like to investigate how these triangles could be folded up to make three-dimensional shapes. Extend this activity by using straws to make squares. How many are needed to make one, two or three squares? Is there a pattern?

Calculator numbers The children could work in small groups with the Valiant Turtle or Roamer to check their results. Also, the instructions for each of the numbers could be read out in PE and the children could walk the numbers together. If there is no

Roamer or Turtle in the school, the children could make a miniature space alien and give him instructions to drive around the numbers in his space buggy! For example, forward 5 squares, right 90° and so on.

Post a shape The children could discuss how their design problems were overcome. They may like to test out their designs and the effectiveness of their boxes with younger pupils. Can the children make an enormous class post-box with large shapes? This could be the focus of an assembly on 'Shape'.

Can you find it? This is an ideal class game for children to play in pairs. It will encourage them to use precise language and measurement. Another game which can be played in class involves having a line of shapes (pegged on a washing line is ideal) and then asking children to describe one. The other children then have to guess which one they are describing. Depending on how hard you want to make the game, the shapes may vary. For example, you can have several different sorts of quadrilateral, or several different sorts of pentagon. This will force the children to say things *other* than 'It has five sides...'.

Fitting boxes The children may like to work in small groups to design boxes using different shapes. Nets which could also form the basis of stacking sets of boxes, including a cube, cuboid and more complex three-dimensional shapes, are provided on pages 92–94 of this book. This task will require co-operation and careful planning.

The right place Ask the children to make a map of the local area. This can be

divided up using a grid. This will encourage map reading and the correct use of grid references. Study a local Ordnance Survey map or an A–Z map. Both of these are based on a grid. Some towns here and in the USA are designed around a grid system – for example, Milton Keynes.

Hidden treasure The children could play this game in pairs in class. This game can be extended by making the grid larger, or 'burying' more than one piece of treasure. A similar game is where the children have a grid each and they have to draw particular things on their grid and then get others to draw the same things in the same places on their grids without looking, just by following a series of coordinate instructions, such as, 'Draw a cat in (4, 7)'.

_____and

child

_____

helper(s)

_____

did this activity together

Compass UK

● Ask someone at home to help you mark your town or village on this map. You may like to use an atlas to help you.

● Can you mark another favourite place on the map?

● Imagine that you are a bird.

● In which direction would you need to travel from home to arrive at your favourite place on the map?

● In which direction would you need to travel in order to come home?

A bird's-eye view of home

● Can you draw a bird's-eye view of your home?

● At midday the sun will be shining from the south. Cut out and stick this compass on to your map of home to show in which direction your home faces.

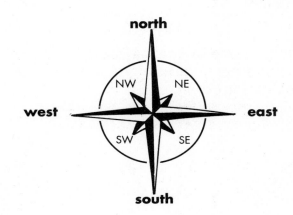

Dear Parent or Carer

You may like to help your child to draw the bird's-eye view of your home. Discuss the general shape of the building – is it a square or an oblong? Help may be needed to stick on the compass. Talk to your child about which side of the building receives the most sunlight, and which side is the coldest.

National Curriculum reference:
Maths Attainment Target
Shape, space and measures

_____and

child

_____

helper(s)

_____

did this activity together

_____and

child

_____

helper(s)

_____

did this activity together

Church

Many Church of England (Anglican) churches are built facing in a particular compass direction.

● Make a drawing of your local church.

● Are you able to work out in which direction the church faces?

● How did you do this?

● Show on your drawing in which direction the church faces.

> HINT: The church may have a weather vane to help you.

Triangular sandwiches

YOU WILL NEED: two slices of bread, some margarine and filling to make a sandwich. PLEASE ASK FIRST!

● Cut your sandwich into four triangles.

● Arrange them carefully so that they make a bigger triangular shape.

● Draw the shape carefully.

● How many more sandwiches do you think you would need to make the next-sized triangle?

Dear Parent or Carer

Please give your child time to arrange the sandwiches before you make any suggestions.
Do the sandwiches fit together without leaving spaces?

National Curriculum reference:
Maths Attainment Target
Shape, space and measures

_____and

child

_____

helper(s)

_____

did this activity together

Shadows

YOU WILL NEED *several sheets of
newspaper, some sticky tape, a
felt-tipped pen, some stones and
somebody to help you.*

● *Stick the sheets of newspaper together
to make a long sheet of paper.*

● *Outside, stand still while someone
draws your shadow on the paper. Hold
the paper in position with the stones.*

● *Is your shadow larger, shorter or
the same size as you are? How can
you find out?*

● *Record the time when your shadow
was drawn on these clocks.*

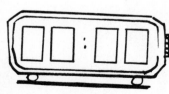

● *Bring your shadow drawings
into class.*

impact MATHS HOMEWORK

Circle symmetry

● Make some circles by drawing round a mug or saucer and then cutting them out.

● Fold or cut your circles into halves or quarters.

● Colour some of your parts of circles.

● Can you use your shapes to create a pattern?

● Here are a few ideas to start you off:

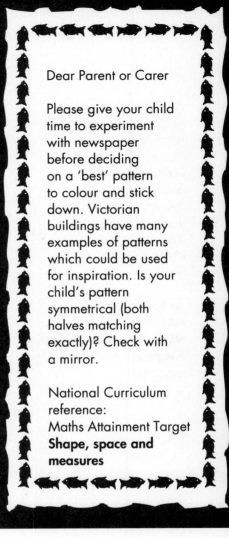

Dear Parent or Carer

Please give your child time to experiment with newspaper before deciding on a 'best' pattern to colour and stick down. Victorian buildings have many examples of patterns which could be used for inspiration. Is your child's pattern symmetrical (both halves matching exactly)? Check with a mirror.

National Curriculum reference:
Maths Attainment Target
Shape, space and measures

_____and

child

_____

helper(s)

_____

did this activity together

Triangle letters

● Using only triangles, can you create
the letters of your name?

Kate has done hers:

● Make your triangle name as much
fun as you can!

● Bring your design back into school.

impact MATHS HOMEWORK

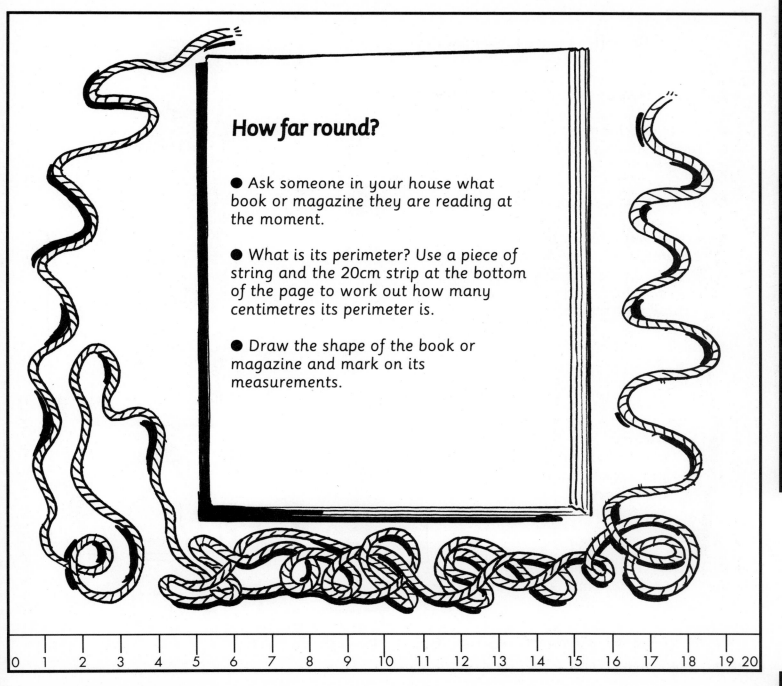

How far round?

● Ask someone in your house what book or magazine they are reading at the moment.

● What is its perimeter? Use a piece of string and the 20cm strip at the bottom of the page to work out how many centimetres its perimeter is.

● Draw the shape of the book or magazine and mark on its measurements.

0 1 2 3 4 5 6 7 8 9 10 11 12 13 14 15 16 17 18 19 20

Dear Parent or Carer

We are working on the different perimeters which different shapes have. The perimeter is the distance around a shape. Help your child to measure with accuracy.

National Curriculum reference:
Maths Attainment Target
Shape, space and measures

_____and

child

_____

helper(s)

_____

did this activity together

_____and

child

_____

helper(s)

_____

did this activity together

Regular or not!

● Choose someone to work with you.

● Decide which one of you is going to
be 'regular shapes' and which one is
going to be 'irregular shapes'!

● Choose a shape from the list below.

● Both of you must draw it. The
person who is 'regular shapes' must
draw a regular example of that shape.
The person who is 'irregular shapes'
must draw an irregular example.

● Check each other's drawings!

Shape list

**triangle
quadrilateral
pentagon
hexagon
septagon**

● Draw at least three shapes from
the list. Colour them in and bring
them back into school.

impact MATHS HOMEWORK

Vertical

- What does a builder use to check that his walls are vertical? How can you check that the walls of your home are vertical?

- Can you design something that helps you to check if surfaces are vertical?

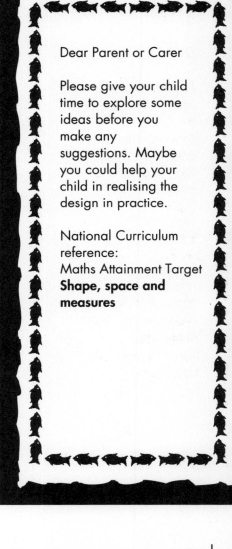

Dear Parent or Carer

Please give your child time to explore some ideas before you make any suggestions. Maybe you could help your child in realising the design in practice.

National Curriculum reference:
Maths Attainment Target
Shape, space and measures

_____and

child

_____

helper(s)

_____

did this activity together

_____and

child

_____

helper(s)

_____

did this activity together

Reflecting squares

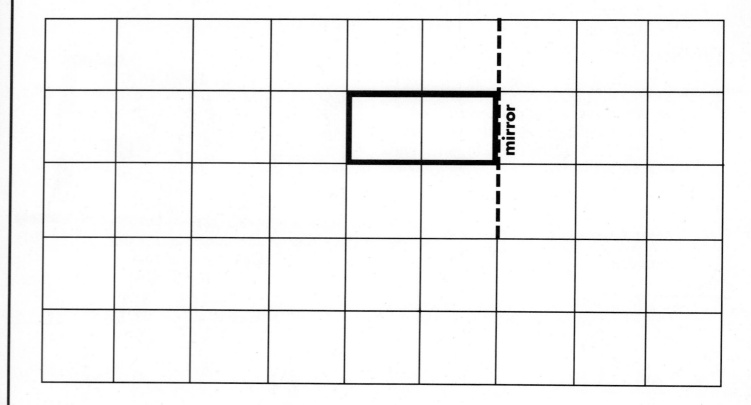

● Place a mirror on the dotted line.

● How many squares can you see?

● Draw in the reflected squares and
shade them in carefully.

● Can you place your mirror in such a
position that you are able to see three
squares from two squares?

● Draw some further reflections with
your mirror and two squares.

impact MATHS HOMEWORK

Straws

YOU WILL NEED: some straws or strips of card or used matches.

● How many straws will you need to make two triangles joined together?

● Carefully draw your two triangles.

● Can you make four triangles?

● How many straws did you use?

● What is the smallest number of straws needed to make four triangles?

Dear Parent or Carer

Please give your child time to experiment with the straws before recording their work. Your child should be encouraged to predict the number of straws needed, before making the triangles.

National Curriculum reference:
Maths Attainment Target
Shape, space and measures

_____and
child

_____
helper(s)

_____
did this activity together

_____and

child

_____

helper(s)

_____

did this activity together

Calculator numbers

● Write all the numbers as they appear on the calculator on the squared grid.

● Can you write instructions for the Roamer or the Turtle to copy any one of the numbers?

● Please remember that the Turtle can only move forwards or backwards and make 90° turns. (One unit of movement is 30cm.)

five

impact MATHS HOMEWORK

Post a shape

YOU WILL NEED: several old boxes or packets.

● Try to design and make a box which will allow you to post different solid shapes.

Things to think about:

• the size of the box;
• whether you will be able to remove the three-dimensional shapes you have posted;
• which small shapes you are going to post.

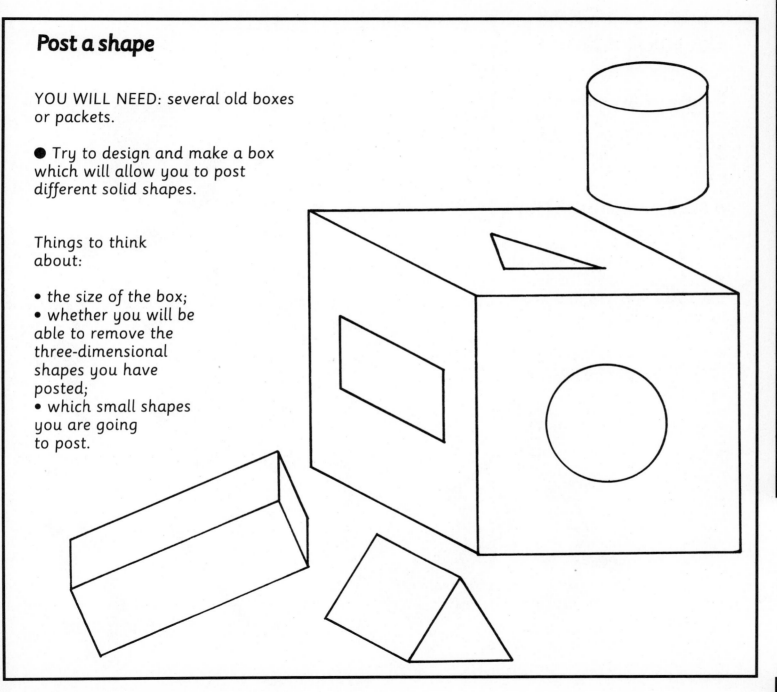

Dear Parent or Carer

Please give your child time to plan carefully before beginning the task. It may be helpful to design with old paper before trying with cardboard from a cereal box or old birthday cards.

National Curriculum reference:
Maths Attainment Target
Shape, space and measures

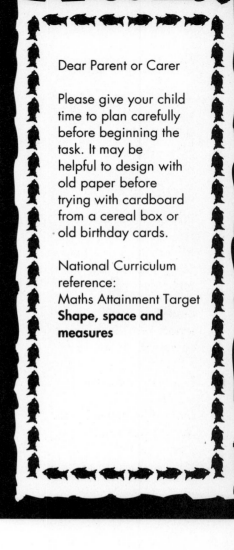

_____and

child

_____

helper(s)

_____

did this activity together

Can you find it?

A game for two players.

YOU WILL NEED: a sheet of paper,
a pencil, a counter, a ruler and
a big book.

● Place the counter on the paper
without your partner seeing it. Put
up the big book as a divider.

● Your partner should ask
questions to try to find the
location of the counter.

● How quickly can your partner
find out the position of the
counter?

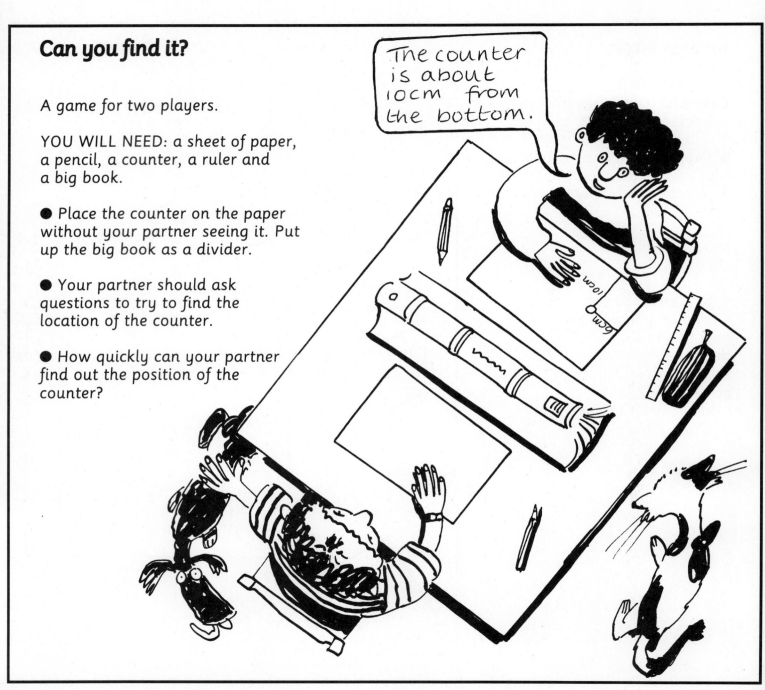

Fitting boxes

● Design three boxes that will fit one inside the other. Old Christmas or birthday cards or a cereal box will provide suitable card.

● You may like to use this net to get you started.

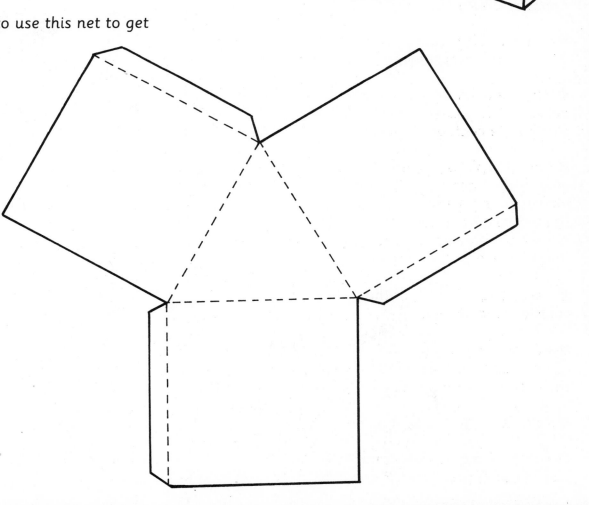

Dear Parent or Carer

It may be useful to use newspaper to try out different sized and shaped nets before cutting the card.

National Curriculum reference:
Maths Attainment Target
Shape, space and measures

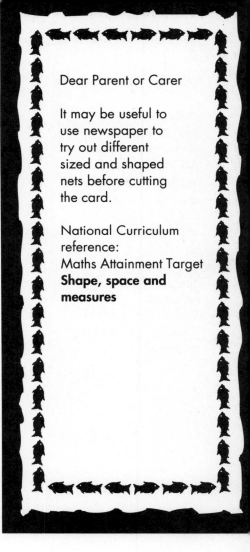

_____and

child

_____

helper(s)

_____

did this activity together

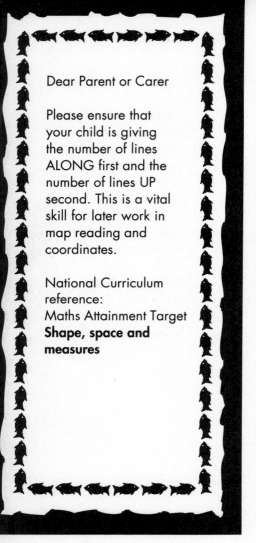
The right place

A game for two players.

YOU WILL NEED: four or five counters each, the playing grids opposite and a big book.

● Cut out the playing grids and give one to each player.

● Put the book up as a divider between the players so that they cannot see each other's grid.

● The first player places a counter where two lines meet and gives instructions for the second player to place their counter in the same place on their grid. For example, 'Along 3, Up 2'.

● Keep playing until all the counters are placed.

● Remove the divider and check the positions of the counters. Are they the same on both grids?

● Take turns to be the caller.

Remember to give the number of lines ALONG first and UP second.

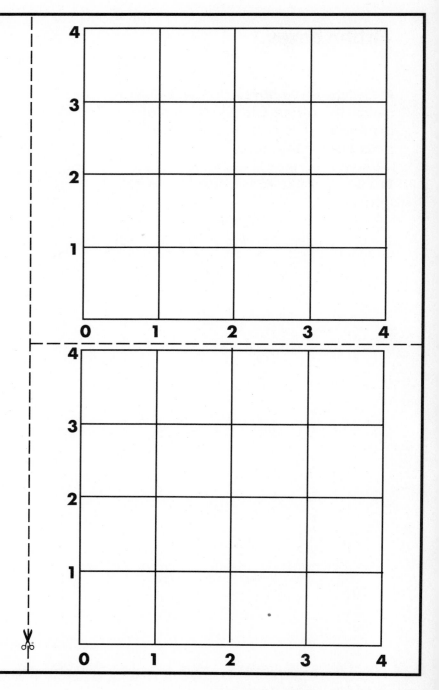

Hidden treasure

● Cut out a grid for each player.

● In any one square on your grid, draw a 'treasure'. Hold your grid so that your helper cannot see it.

● Your helper, who has the second grid, must start from any one of the corners and attempt to locate the treasure. They can only move one square to the right, to the left or forwards at a time.

● Each move should be read out and drawn on the individual grids by you and your helper. (These can be checked at the end of the game.)

● You reply, 'Hotter' if the move takes your helper nearer the treasure and 'Colder' if the move takes your helper further away from the treasure.

● How many moves does your helper need to find the treasure?

✂

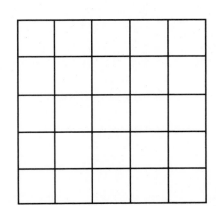

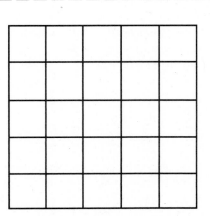

Dear Parent or Carer

Your child may need some assistance in making the moves. It may be helpful to trace some of the moves with a finger or walk them through before playing the game.

National Curriculum reference:
Maths Attainment Target
Shape, space and measures

_____and
child

_____
helper(s)

_____
did this activity together

Teachers' notes
YEAR FIVE

Letter rotation The children can compare the letters. Do they agree which ones have line symmetry and which ones have rotational symmetry only (such as 'S' and 'Z'). They can make three sets and pin large cut out letters in them – one set of non-symmetrical letters, one set of letters with line symmetry and one set of letters with rotational symmetry. Which set has most letters in it? What about lower case letters? What about numerals?

Trapezium tessellation Compare the children's patterns. Then look at the lines of symmetry in the trapezium. Is there any connection between the number of lines of symmetry and whether a shape will tessellate? Which other regular shapes tessellate? Look at different quadrilaterals. Squares are a special type of rectangle, rectangles are a special type of parallelogram, parallelograms are a special type of trapezium and so on. A trapezium has one pair of parallel sides. A parallelogram has two pairs of parallel sides. A rhombus has four equal sides and a square has four equal sides and four right angles. Draw a Venn diagram to show as many types of quadrilateral as you can (see Figure 1).

Make a net The children can work in groups to make a definitive set of all the arrangements of six squares which fold up to make a cube. (A basic cube net is provided on page 92 for making cube models.) Then they can make a set of all the arrangements of six squares which do *not* fold up to make a cube! Are they sure which ones go where? (NB: there is one arrangement of squares which makes a cube and which has a horizontal line of only two squares –   .)

Straw pyramids Encourage the children to use circles, pentagons and so on for the bases of their pyramids. Then they could sort their pyramids using various criteria, such as the shapes of bases. How many types of pyramids have been constructed? The children may like to make replicas of their pyramids using Polydron or a similar construction kit. Their models would make attractive mobiles. A cone is really a special type of pyramid. So is a tetrahedron. A tetrahedron makes a good die since all four faces are the same shape. What other solid shapes have all their faces the same?

Shape grid The children can compare the shapes they have drawn. Let them colour their grids and then display them. Remind the children that any five-sided shape is a pentagon, any six-sided shape is a hexagon and so on. A regular shape, such as a regular hexagon or pentagon, is one with equal sides. Rectangles are particular sorts of quadrilateral. Both squares and oblongs are rectangles. Talk about the different types of quadrilaterals – parallelograms, trapezia, rhombuses and so on. The Venn diagram below (Figure 1) can be used to help the children to sort them and to see the relationships between the different types.

Square, oblong, triangle The children can discuss the different shapes that they made and then cut them out and classify them in sets according to the number of sides. Talk about which of the quadrilaterals are regular shapes. Both squares and oblongs are rectangles, but, strictly speaking, only squares are regular (with equal sides and equal angles). Look at different triangles. Which ones are regular? Which ones have two equal sides (isoceles)? Which ones have a right angle? Which have an angle of more than 90°?

Eight royal knights The children can discuss the lines of symmetry in their moves. What does it look like to rotate the 'knight' shape by 90°, by 180°, by 270° and by 360°? What does it look like to flip the shape over so that it makes its own mirror image? How many different positions can the children put the 'knight' in by rotating and flipping it around a common origin? Draw all of these on a large grid and display it on the wall. Try a different shape. How about this one:

Let the children try rotating this, flipping it over and translating it (sliding it along). What patterns can they make?

Horizontal Please allow the children time to demonstrate the effectiveness of their designs. It may be possible to bring a spirit-level into school to show the children. The children may like to construct a flat surface in the classroom, using bricks, blocks, books or any other construction equipment, and check if it is horizontal with the spirit-level. They can also look for vertical lines and check these by measuring the angle between the horizontal and the vertical. Where can they see right angles in the classroom?

Rotate an oblong The children may like to draw and cut out a picture of an animal or a plant and rotate their cut out shape in a similar way to the oblong. They could turn their bodies through 90° in a PE lesson. What will they see on the wall if they turn 90°? Can the children find other shapes which they can rotate through 90°? Which shapes make the most interesting patterns?

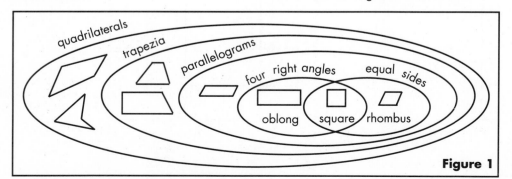

Figure 1

Try shapes which themselves have a right angle – for example:

Half an oblong The children can compare the halves. What shapes are they? Did they realise that there are an infinite number of ways of folding the oblong in half? Mount all their shapes in appropriate sets, headed 'squares', 'oblongs', 'triangles' and so on. If they try folding a triangle in half, what shapes do they get then? Try to describe all the different triangles obtained by folding an equilateral triangle in half. (Equilateral triangles have equal sides and three angles of 60°.)

Divided oblong The children can discuss the different shapes they managed to make. What shapes are possible when a rectangle is divided using just one straight line? What about using two straight lines? Display all the possible shapes under the appropriate classification. The children can try dividing other quadrilaterals in half. What about a square? What about a trapezium? How about trying to divide an arrow shape in half?

Encourage them to try as many different quadrilaterals as they can and display the different shapes they get by dividing them in half.

Divided hexagon The children can discuss the different shapes they managed to make. What shapes are possible when a hexagon is divided using just one straight line? What about using two straight lines?

Discuss the different examples of hexagons – which one is regular? Display all the possible shapes under the appropriate classification. Some of the children – those who have really enjoyed this activity – can try dividing a different shape, such as a pentagon. What shapes do they get then? Can these be classified and displayed? Can the children pick one and describe it? Guess which one they are describing.

Regular tessellation The children can compare their patterns. They can then look at the lines of symmetry in their shapes and in all the regular shapes. A regular shape is one which has equal sides and equal angles. Is there any connection between the number of lines of symmetry and whether a shape will or will not tessellate? Which other common irregular shapes will tessellate? It is important to recognise that there are different definitions of regular – an oblong is regular if we are looking at two lines of symmetry, but it is irregular if we are looking for equal sides. What about a circle?

Tessellating hexagons The children can compare their examples of tessellation. Then they can look at the lines of symmetry in their shapes and in the different hexagons. Is there any connection between the number of lines of symmetry and whether a shape will or will not tessellate? Which other regular shapes tessellate; for example, do regular pentagons tessellate? What about other pentagons? How about octogons? Victorian designers tessellated octogons by putting small squares in the 'gaps'. Are there any other shapes where the gaps have to be filled like this?

How many triangles? The children can make a massive class triangle made up of lots and lots of smaller triangles! Can they predict how many it will contain if they know the number of rows? Can they colour this massive triangle using only four colours? 'The four colour theorem' has been demonstrated many times, but never proved. So it is theoretically possible that one day someone will discover a pattern which cannot be coloured using only four colours so that no two shapes of the same colour are touching.

Hexagon of hexagons The children can make a massive class hexagon made up of lots and lots of smaller hexagons! Talk with them about similar shapes. Can they predict how many small hexagons it will contain if they know the length of the sides? Can they colour this massive hexagon using only four colours? 'The four colour theorem' has been demonstrated many times, but never proved. So it is theoretically possible that one day someone will discover a pattern which cannot be coloured using four colours so that no two shapes of the same colour are touching.

_____and

child

_____

helper(s)

_____

did this activity together

Letter rotation

● Write your name in capital letters.

● Look at the letters.

● Which letters have rotational symmetry?

● If there are none in your name, try someone else's name!

● Which letters have line symmetry?

● Draw in the lines of symmetry in any letters in your name.

impact MATHS HOMEWORK

Trapezium tessellation

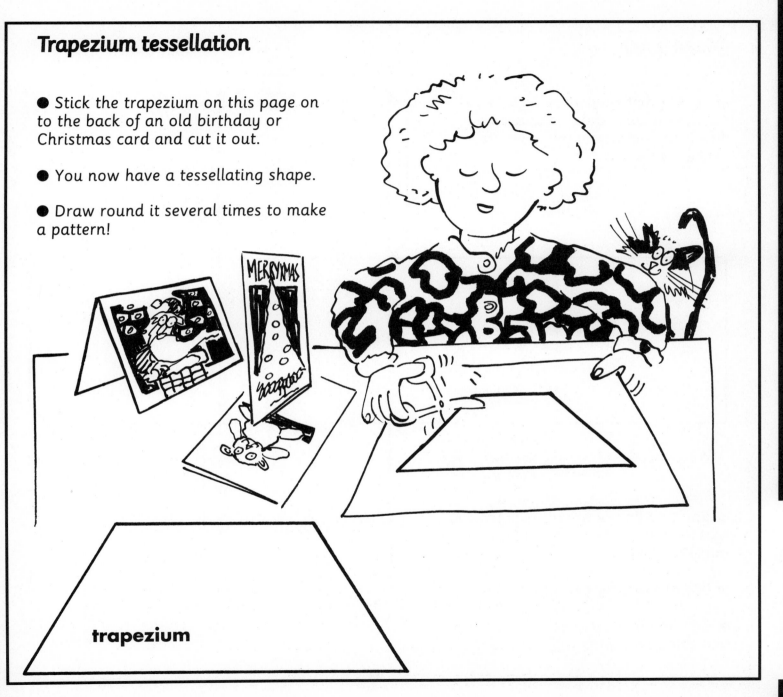

- Stick the trapezium on this page on to the back of an old birthday or Christmas card and cut it out.

- You now have a tessellating shape.

- Draw round it several times to make a pattern!

trapezium

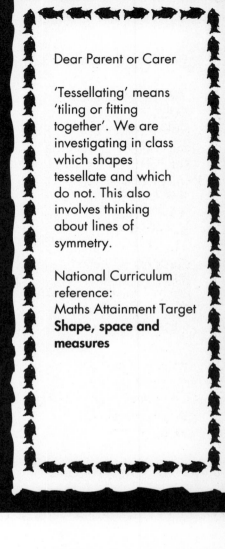

Dear Parent or Carer

'Tessellating' means 'tiling or fitting together'. We are investigating in class which shapes tessellate and which do not. This also involves thinking about lines of symmetry.

National Curriculum reference:
Maths Attainment Target
Shape, space and measures

_____and

child

_____

helper(s)

_____

did this activity together

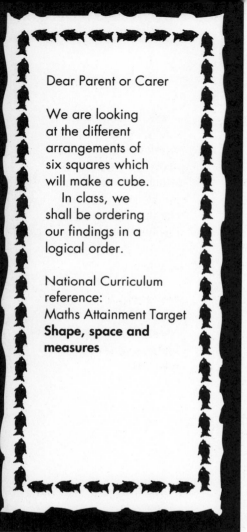
Make a net

A net is a flat shape which folds up to make a solid shape. For example, this is the net commonly given to make a cube.

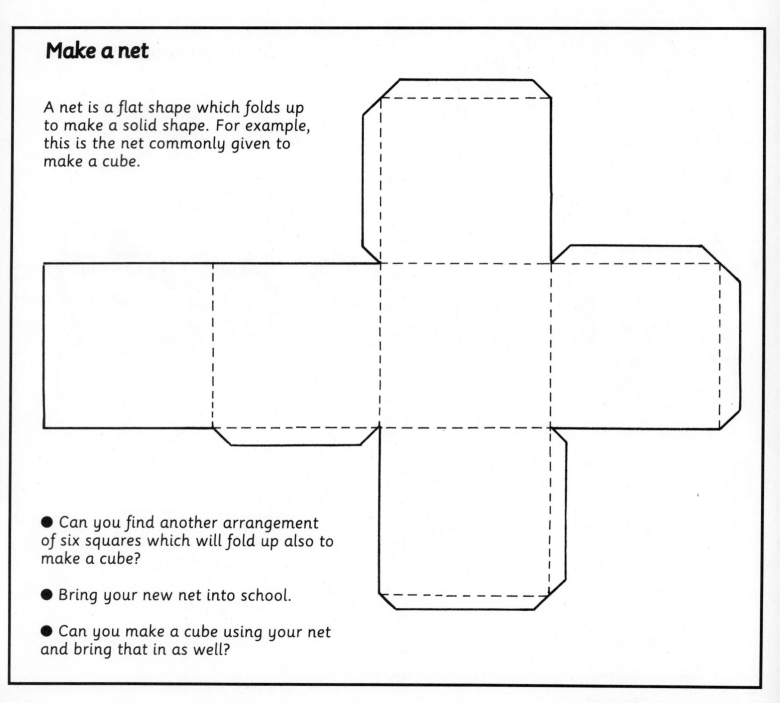

● Can you find another arrangement of six squares which will fold up also to make a cube?

● Bring your new net into school.

● Can you make a cube using your net and bring that in as well?

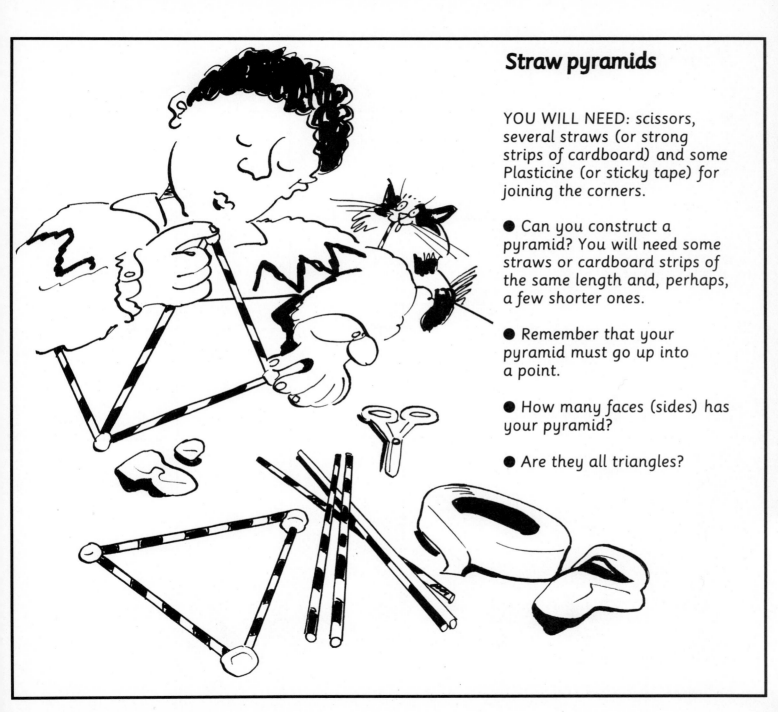

Straw pyramids

YOU WILL NEED: scissors, several straws (or strong strips of cardboard) and some Plasticine (or sticky tape) for joining the corners.

● Can you construct a pyramid? You will need some straws or cardboard strips of the same length and, perhaps, a few shorter ones.

● Remember that your pyramid must go up into a point.

● How many faces (sides) has your pyramid?

● Are they all triangles?

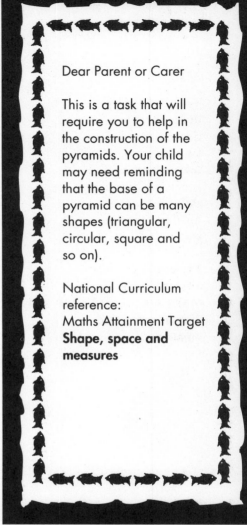

_____and

child

_____

helper(s)

_____

did this activity together

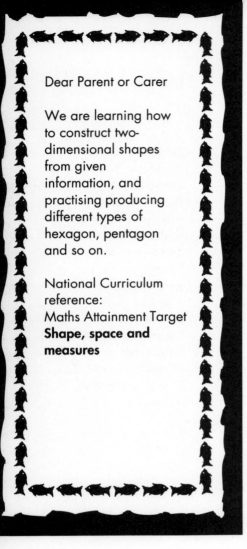

Dear Parent or Carer

We are learning how to construct two-dimensional shapes from given information, and practising producing different types of hexagon, pentagon and so on.

National Curriculum reference:
Maths Attainment Target
Shape, space and measures

_____and

child

_____

helper(s)

_____

did this activity together

Shape grid

● Draw shapes in the grid opposite so that every row and every column contains a hexagon, a pentagon, a quadrilateral and a triangle.

● BUT none of the shapes must look identical!

impact MATHS HOMEWORK

Square, oblong, triangle

● Cut out the shapes at the bottom of the page to use as templates.

● How many different two-dimensional shapes can you create using two or three of the shapes.

● Can you draw and name them all?

● Bring all your shape drawings back into school.

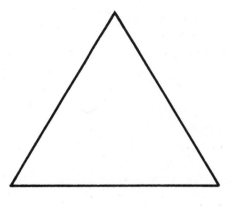

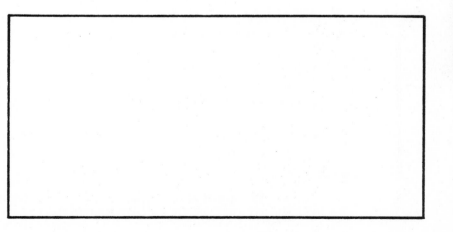

Dear Parent or Carer

We are exploring the properties of various flat (two-dimensional) shapes. A pentagon is any five-sided shape, a hexagon is any six-sided shape and so on. Regular pentagons or hexagons are the ones with sides of equal length.

National Curriculum reference:
Maths Attainment Target
Shape, space and measures

_____and

child

_____

helper(s)

_____

did this activity together

Eight royal knights

A game for two players.

YOU WILL NEED: both 'knights' on this page, cut out and coloured in, the 8 × 8 grid provided and a pencil each.

● The aim of this game is to move your 'knight' from its starting position on the grid and visit as many squares as possible until no more moves can be made.

• Decide who is going to be 'noughts' and who is going to be 'crosses'. Take turns to move. Each time a move is made, mark its position with either noughts or crosses as appropriate.

• When your 'knight' makes its next move, at least one square's edge of it must remain touching one square's edge of its previous position.

• Once a square has been used by either player it cannot be used again.

• The winner is the last player able to make a move.

● Draw another grid and play again – or rub out your noughts and crosses and use the same board!

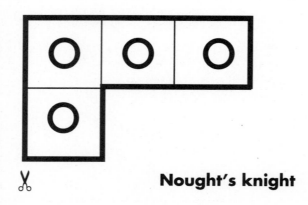

Nought's knight

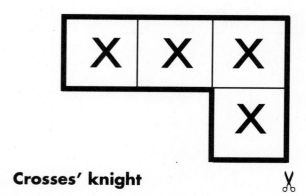

Crosses' knight

Eight royal knights

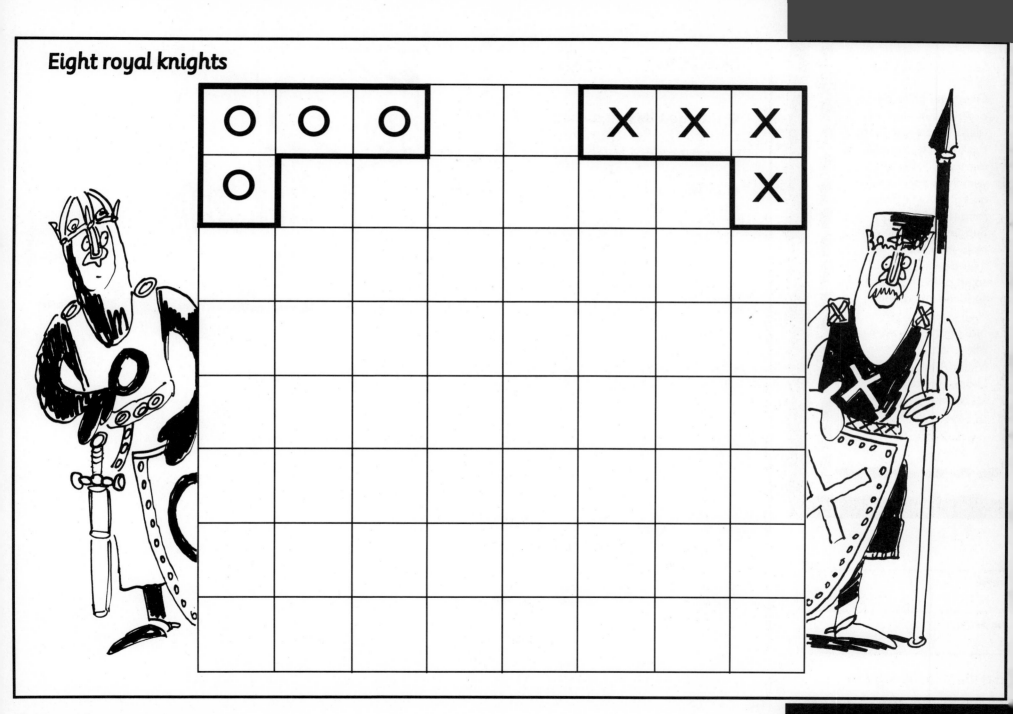

_____and

child

_____

helper(s)

_____

did this activity together

Horizontal

● Can you design something to check that all the flat (horizontal) surfaces in your home are level?

● In the space below, draw three things that are level.

impact MATHS HOMEWORK

Rotate an oblong

● Cut out the oblong at the bottom of the page.

● Place the oblong on the lines as shown in figure 1.

Figure 1

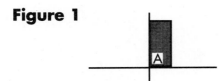

● Now write the letter A in the corner of the oblong as shown.

● Draw round the oblong and then rotate it into the next corner (*see figure 2*) and draw round it.

Figure 2

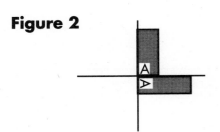

● Keep rotating it until you have drawn four oblongs.

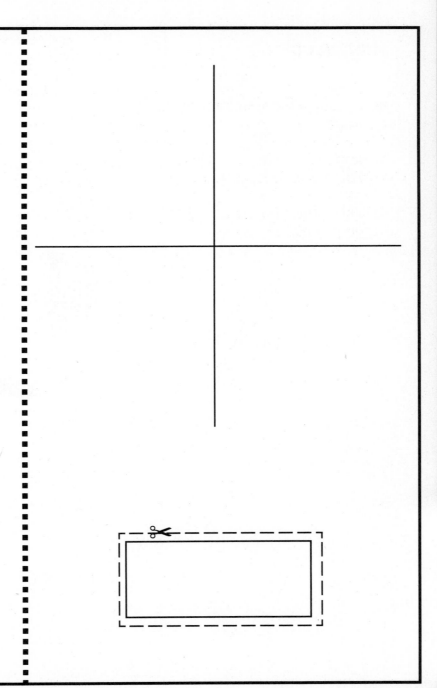

Dear Parent or Carer

Your child may need help to rotate the oblong. Ask your child how many times the oblong will need to be rotated through 90° before it returns to its original position.

National Curriculum reference:
Maths Attainment Target
Shape, space and measures

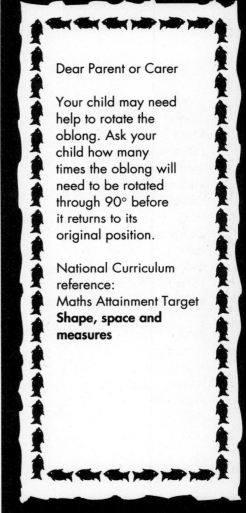

_____and

child

_____

helper(s)

_____

did this activity together

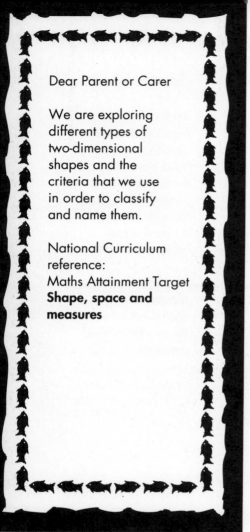
Half an oblong

● Cut out several oblong pieces of paper.

● How many ways are there of folding these in half?

● What shapes are each of the different halves?

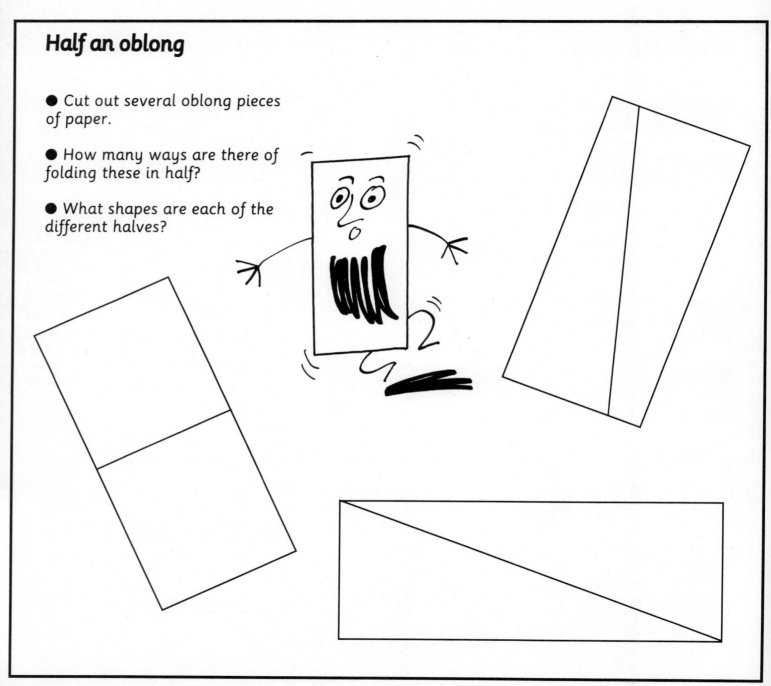

impact MATHS HOMEWORK

Divided oblong

- Draw an oblong below.

- Your helper must divide it into two, not necessarily equal, pieces by drawing a straight line across it.

- What shapes can you now see?

- Are both the pieces triangles?

- Or are they quadrilaterals (four-sided shapes) and, if so, what sort (that is, squares, oblongs, parallelograms and so on)?

- Ask your helper to draw another oblong.

- Divide it using one straight line. Can you make differently-shaped parts?

- Try using two lines – what shapes do you get now?

- Bring all your drawings into school.

Dear Parent or Carer

We are working in class on recognising and talking about different shapes. All four-sided shapes are quadrilaterals – the most common examples are rectangles which can be either squares or oblongs! All three-sided shapes are triangles!

National Curriculum reference:
Maths Attainment Target
Shape, space and measures

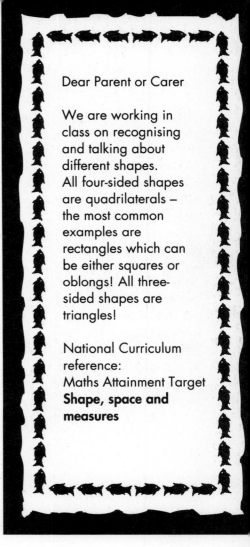

_____and

child

_____

helper(s)

_____

did this activity together

_____and

child

_____

helper(s)

_____

did this activity together

Divided hexagon

● Draw a hexagon (that is, a six-sided shape).

● Your helper must divide it into two, not necessarily equal, pieces by drawing a straight line across it.

● What shapes can you now see?

● Are both the pieces triangles?

● Or are they quadrilaterals (four-sided shapes) and, if so, what sort (that is, squares, oblongs, parallelograms and so on)?

● Ask your helper to draw another hexagon.

● Divide it using one straight line. Can you make differently-shaped parts?

● How many different shapes can you create by dividing a hexagon?

● Does it make any difference which shaped hexagon you start with?

● Try two lines – what shapes do you get now?

● Bring all your drawings into school.

Regular tessellation

- Which regular shapes will tessellate?

- To answer this question you will need to think about which shapes are regular shapes (and why!) and whether or not they will tessellate.

- Bring at least one example of a tessellation pattern into school.

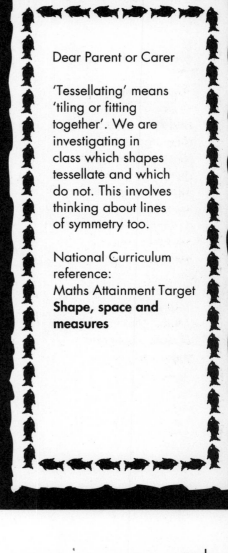

Dear Parent or Carer

'Tessellating' means 'tiling or fitting together'. We are investigating in class which shapes tessellate and which do not. This involves thinking about lines of symmetry too.

National Curriculum reference:
Maths Attainment Target
Shape, space and measures

_____and

child

_____

helper(s)

_____

did this activity together

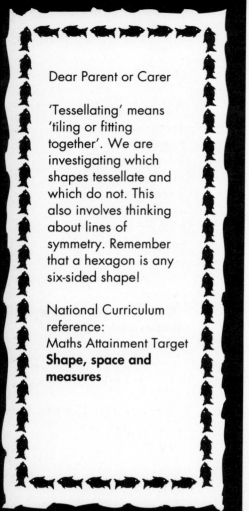
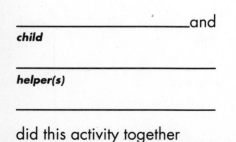

_____and

child

_____

helper(s)

_____

did this activity together

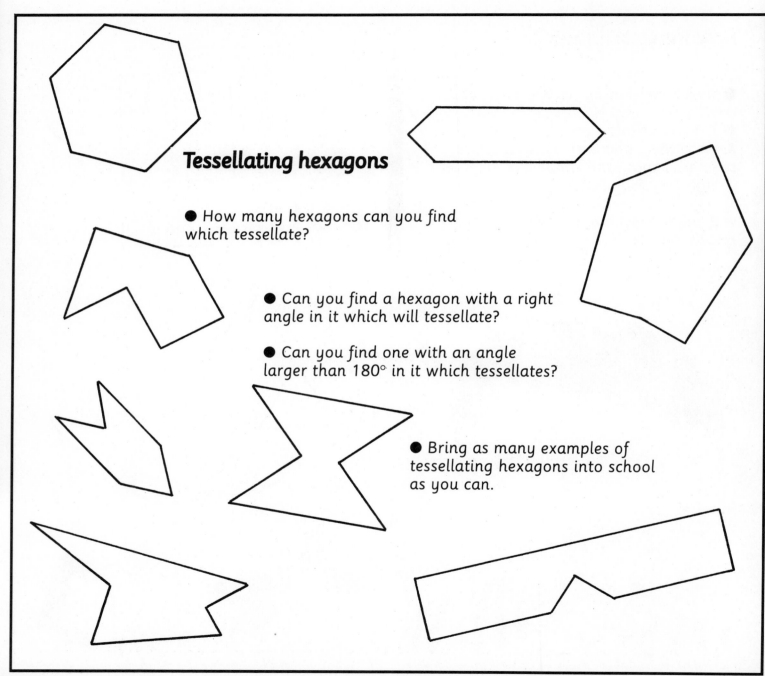

Tessellating hexagons

● How many hexagons can you find which tessellate?

● Can you find a hexagon with a right angle in it which will tessellate?

● Can you find one with an angle larger than 180° in it which tessellates?

● Bring as many examples of tessellating hexagons into school as you can.

How many triangles?

● Make a large triangle consisting of many equilateral triangles!

● How many small triangles are there in it, if it has four rows?

● Make a large equilateral triangle with eight rows.

● Can you predict how many triangles there will be in it?

● Colour it in using only four colours, so that no triangle is touching edge to edge with another triangle of the same colour.

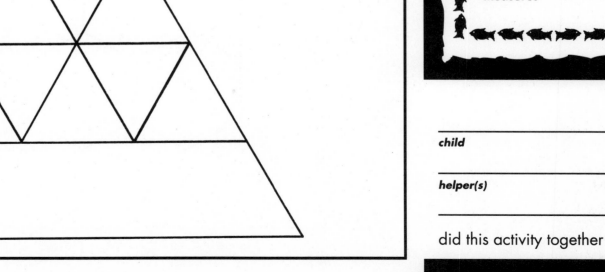

Dear Parent or Carer

There is a famous mathematical theorem called 'The four colour theorem'. This states that any map (or pattern of shapes) can be coloured in such a way as to ensure that no shape touches a shape of the same colour when using only four colours. We are demonstrating the truth of this!

National Curriculum reference:
Maths Attainment Target
Shape, space and measures

_____and
child

_____
helper(s)

_____
did this activity together

_____and

child

_____

helper(s)

_____

did this activity together

Hexagon of hexagons

The hexagon below is made up entirely of similar shapes.

● Can you design and draw an even larger one? Use the triangular paper provided. How many hexagons does your pattern contain?

● Colour it in using only four colours so that no hexagon is touching edge to edge with another hexagon of the same colour.

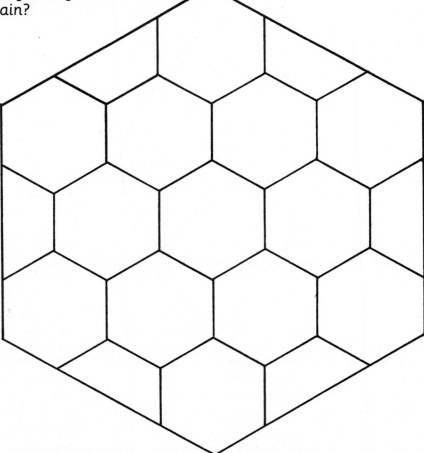

impact MATHS HOMEWORK

Teachers' notes
YEAR SIX

Diagonal count-up The children will need squared paper for this activity at home and in the classroom. They can work in groups in class to try out different types of oblong. Try a whole series in which the shorter side is three squares long. Then try a series in which the shorter side is four squares long, and so on. Encourage the children to record their findings systematically. This activity is really about recording and then making sensible predictions. In fact, the easiest patterns to be found are discovered if the width of the rectangle is kept constant whilst the length is varied.

Tetrahedron capacity The tetrahedron net is given on page 92, as well as on the activity page. In class, the children can compare their answers for the capacity. Did they all get the same? What is the size difference between their answers and how do they account for these? Can they make another solid shape using one of the other nets provided on pages 92–94? Ask them to decorate their shapes and hang them up. Can they measure the volume of some other solid shapes? How will they do this if the shape cannot be opened and shut – by displacement perhaps.

Octahedron capacity Each child will need a copy of the octahedron net, on page 93, for this activity. They can compare their answers for the capacity. Did they all get the same? What is the size difference between their answers and how do they account for these? Can they make another solid shape using one of the other nets provided on pages 92–94? Ask them to decorate their shapes and hang them up. Count the number of faces on each shape. How many corners does each one have? How many edges? Add the corners and the faces and subtract the number of edges. Try this for lots of different shapes. You should always get 2. This is known as 'Euler's constant'.

Dodecahedron capacity Each child will need a copy of the dodecahedron net, on page 93, for this activity. They can compare their answers for the capacity. Did they all get the same? What is the size difference between their answers and how do they account for these? Can they make another solid shape using one of the other nets provided on pages 92–94? Ask them to decorate their shapes and hang them up. Count the number of faces on each shape. How many corners does each one have? How many edges? Add the corners and the faces and subtract the number of edges. Try this for lots of different shapes. You should always get 2. This is known as 'Euler's constant'.

Three sides only The children can compare their triangles. Then they can cut them out and arrange them in three sets: those with only acute angles, those with right angles, those with obtuse angles.

Talk about these different angles. Always refer to the right angle as the 'bench-mark' by which we can recognise if an angle is acute or obtuse. Talk about angles which are greater than 180°. These are called 'reflex angles'. What shapes can they draw which contain a reflex angle?

Four sides only The children can compare their quadrilaterals. Then they can cut them out and arrange them in sets: those which are rectangular (this includes squares and oblongs), those which contain obtuse angles and those which only contain acute or right angles. Can the children draw a quadrilateral which contains a reflex angle? A reflex angle must be over 180°. Can they draw a trapezium with a right angle in it? Why is a quadrilateral which has only acute angles impossible?

Six sides only The children can compare their hexagons. Then they can cut them out and arrange them according to the type of angles they contain – that is, obtuse angles, acute angles or right angles. Can they describe some of the different shapes they discover? Which ones have two sides of equal length? Which ones have no sides of equal length? Which ones are symmetrical? Give the children specified tasks, such as 'Draw a hexagon containing a right angle and an obtuse angle.' Can they do it? 'Draw a hexagon containing three right angles?' Is this possible? Such instructions focus the mind on the properties of both the angles and the shape.

Smaller but the same! The children can cut up triangles, squares and trapezium shapes and lay the shapes one on top of another to check that they are identical.

Talk about similar shapes – that is, shapes which are the same except for their size. The children can see that each of the small triangles or squares is similar to its 'parent' shape. Can they decide then if there are any other shapes which will produce congruent 'babies' like these three do? Discuss whether the triangle has to be equilateral for it to have 'babies' like this? Obviously a square has equal sides, but will an oblong work? Let them investigate a rhombus (equal sides, but not equal angles).

Reflections The children can try rotating the small pattern squares. What patterns can they produce using rotation? Look at the larger completed grids. Do these have line symmetry or rotational symmetry? Let them start with a different small pattern square – what patterns can they make now? The children can try translating their squares – that is, keeping them as they are and just sliding them along or down. What patterns can they make now? Many common tiling patterns are made by reflecting, rotating or translating a basic square. Encourage the children to find examples.

Nesting pyramids The children can compare their pyramids. Can they work in groups to find out how much each of their pyramids holds? They can find the capacities by using a 5ml (medicine) spoon to fill their pyramids with rice or lentils. How much more do the bigger ones hold than the smaller ones? Don't forget to encourage the children to estimate first! Which one holds the least and which one holds the most?

Acute, obtuse and reflex angles! The children can compare their examples of angles. Did they spot that open doors or cupboard doors, the hands on a clock or the crossed legs of an ironing board all make reflex angles? Which angle is the largest? Which one is the smallest? Use a protractor to measure some angles. Can the children draw some angles and then guess their size? How close are they? Does it make any difference how long the lines are?

Join the dots! The children can compare their shapes. Can they create a pentagon? Can they create a septagon? What happens if they try circles with 24 dots on them. Can they create irregular shapes? How can they do this (for example, join the first dot to the third to the fourth to the sixth and so on)? Look at all the shapes they make. How can the shapes be categorised? Then any children who are brave(!) can create 'mystic roses' by drawing another circle with 12 dots equally spaced around the edge and joining every dot to every other dot with straight lines. (See also 'Roses of mystery' on page 88.) These mystic roses (you get an even more beautiful one with 24 dots) were used as prophylactics in the Middle Ages.

Envelopes These curves make a lovely display. Can the children work in groups to create really large curves using thick thread and drawing pins on large pieces of paper on the wall? Talk about the curves they get. What happens if you alter the angle of the lines? What shapes appear if the angle is small and if it is large? What happens if it is an obtuse angle?

Corner cut-offs! The children can compare their results. Which size corner gives the largest box? If they start with a different sized oblong, can they predict which size corner will give the largest box? Different groups can try out different oblongs in a systematic fashion. What happens with squares?

Icosahedrons! The children can make large examples of these shapes in class. They can decorate them before folding them and sticking them. Hang them up to make a lovely display! Encourage the children to count the number of vertices (corners) on an icosahedron and then to count the edges and the faces. If they add the number of vertices to the number of faces and subtract the number of edges, what number do they get? Let them try this with a cube and with a tetrahedron. This constant is known as 'Euler's constant'.

Roses of mystery The children can compare roses. Discuss why they think they are called 'roses'. Those who are most enthusiastic can try making a real mystic rose by joining all the dots on a circle with 24 dots. Some children can also stitch mystic roses using a needle and thread. These can be very beautiful, especially if sewn on linen.

Ellipse The children can talk about an ellipse and what it looks like. They can try drawing one by putting a loop of thread loosely round two drawing pins (pinned about 3cm apart on a piece of paper on a pinboard) and pulling the loop tight with the pencil and drawing the line they get if they let the pencil travel around the whole loop, keeping the loop pulled tight all the way round. An ellipse – unlike a circle – has two focii.

Kath's sandwiches The children can compare their working out of this problem. Did they all come to the same conclusions? Can they think of better shaped sandwiches for eating in the car?!

Suppose a small child didn't like crusts – which sandwich would be best for them? This is actually a difficult question to answer! Does it make any difference what *size* the sandwiches are? (The answer is no – see below.)

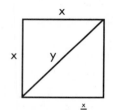

If bread has:
side = x
diagonal = y
$y^2 = 2x^2$
$y = \sqrt{2}x$
$y = 1.4x$

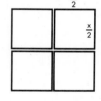

Method 1
crust on each sandwich = x
crumb on each sandwich = x
(that is, $2 \times \frac{x}{2}$)

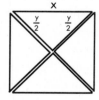

Method 2
crust = x
crumb = y
(that is, $2 \times \frac{y}{2}$)
But $y = 1.4x$

So *proportionately* there is more crumb per crust in method 2 and the sandwich is more likely to hold together in method 1.

Three in a cube The children can stick 27 of their small slanted pyramids together to make one enormous cube! The volume of a cube is the area of its base multiplied by its height. The volume of a pyramid is one third of the area of its base multiplied by its height. Since three pyramids make a cube, the children can see why this is the case. They can prove it using lentils or dry rice to measure the various volumes.

Nets – 1, 2 and 3 Each of these three pages contain two nets. It is suggested that you enlarge the appropriate page to A3 and then copy just the net that you require on to A4 sheets. Enlarging the nets makes them much easier to handle. The nets may be used for work on volume and capacity. The children can find the capacity of any solid shape by filling it with lentils or rice and using a calibrated measuring jar to see how many millilitres it holds. (If you don't have a calibrated measure, a 5ml medicine spoon will do if you count carefully.) Remember that 1ml = 1cm³ (or 1cc). Also, if trying to calculate the volume of a solid shape, any prism – a shape which has a uniform cross-section – has a volume which is equal to the area of the end multiplied by the length (or height).

Diagonal count-up

YOU WILL NEED: 1cm squared paper.

● Draw a diagonal line in on each of these oblongs from corner to corner.

● How many squares does each diagonal cross?

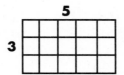

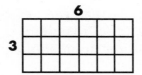

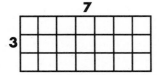

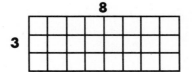

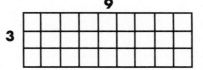

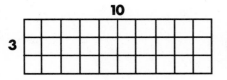

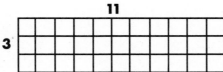

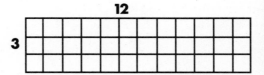

● Draw your own oblong on the squared paper provided. Can you predict how many squares the diagonal will cross?

● Try other oblongs.

● When you think you can predict – at least for some oblongs – how many squares the line will cross, ask someone to help you write it down!

● Bring all your work into school.

Dear Parent or Carer

This is a mathematics investigation. The children are exploring a piece of mathematics in an attempt to make hypotheses and generalisations. Help them get as far as they can. We shall continue to work on this in class!

National Curriculum reference:
Maths Attainment Target
Shape, space and measures

_____and

child

_____

helper(s)

_____

did this activity together

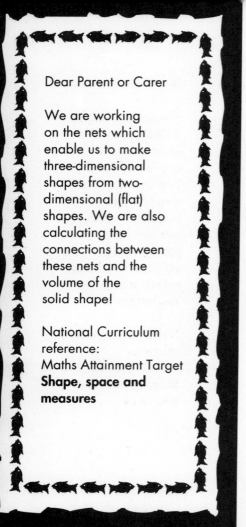
Tetrahedron capacity

● Using the net below, make a tetrahedron.

● Copy or stick the net on to card, cut it out and fold it along the dotted lines to make the solid shape.

● Leave one side unstuck to make a lid or door.

● How much does your tetrahedron hold? Measure its capacity using a 5ml teaspoon (such as a medicine spoon) and rice or lentils or salt or sugar. Carefully count the number of teaspoonfuls and multiply by 5 to find the number of millilitres.

● How much does your tetrahedron hold?

● Bring your tetrahedron and your answer into school.

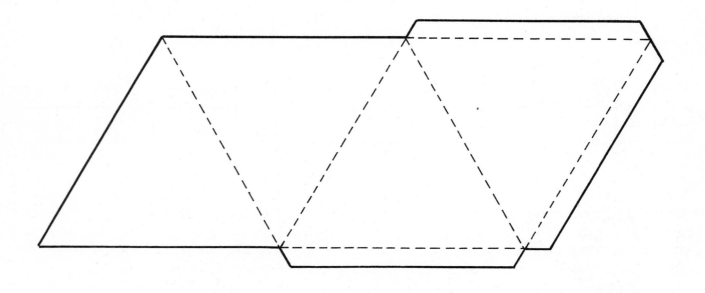

impact MATHS HOMEWORK

Octahedron capacity

● Using the net supplied, make an octahedron.

● Copy or stick the net on to card, cut it out and fold it along the dotted lines to make the solid shape.

● Leave one side unstuck to make a lid or door.

● How much does your octahedron hold? Measure its capacity using a 5ml teaspoon (such as a medicine spoon) and rice or lentils or salt or sugar. Count the number of teaspoonfuls carefully and multiply by 5 to find the number of millilitres.

● How much does your octahedron hold?

● Bring your octahedron and your answer into school.

Dear Parent or Carer

We are working on the nets which enable us to make three-dimensional (solid) shapes from two-dimensional (flat) shapes. We are also calculating the connections between these nets and the volume of the solid shape!

National Curriculum reference:
Maths Attainment Target
Shape, space and measures

_____and

child

_____

helper(s)

_____

did this activity together

_____and

child

_____

helper(s)

_____

did this activity together

Dodecahedron capacity

● Using the net supplied, make
a dodecahedron.

● Copy or stick the net on to card, cut
it out and fold it along the dotted lines
to make the solid shape.

● Leave one side unstuck to make a lid
or door.

● How much does your dodecahedron
hold? Measure its capacity using a 5ml
teaspoon (such as a medicine spoon)
and rice or lentils or salt or sugar.

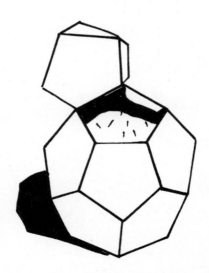

● Carefully count the number of
teaspoonfuls and multiply by 5 to find
the number of millilitres.

● How much does your dodecahedron
hold?

● Bring your dodecahedron and your
answer into school.

impact MATHS HOMEWORK

Three sides only

● Find someone to work with.

● Can you both draw a triangle that has one right angle?

● Can you both draw a triangle with one angle that is bigger than a right angle? This is called an 'obtuse angle'.

● How many different-shaped triangles can you both draw?

● Bring all your drawings into school.

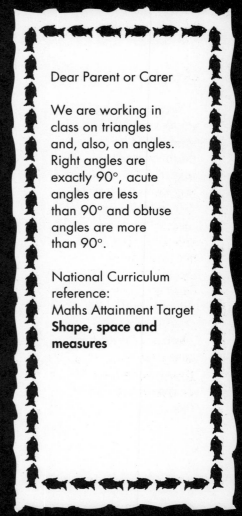

Dear Parent or Carer

We are working in class on triangles and, also, on angles. Right angles are exactly 90°, acute angles are less than 90° and obtuse angles are more than 90°.

National Curriculum reference: Maths Attainment Target **Shape, space and measures**

_____and

child

_____

helper(s)

_____

did this activity together

Four sides only

We call a four-sided shape a 'quadrilateral'.

● Find someone to work with.

● Can you both draw a quadrilateral that has one right angle?

● Can you both draw a quadrilateral that has two right angles?

● Can you both draw a quadrilateral that has three right angles?

● Can you both draw a quadrilateral that has four right angles?

● Can you both draw a quadrilateral with one angle that is bigger than a right angle?

● Can you both draw a quadrilateral with two angles that are bigger than a right angle?

● Can you both draw a quadrilateral with three angles that are bigger than a right angle?

Watch out! Some of these may be impossible!

● Bring all your drawings into school.

Six sides only

We call a six-sided shape a 'hexagon'.

● Find someone to work with.

● Can you both draw a hexagon that has one right angle?

● Can you both draw a hexagon that has two right angles?

● Can you both draw a hexagon that has three right angles?

● Can you both draw a hexagon that has four right angles?

● Can you both draw a hexagon that has five right angles?

● Can you both draw a hexagon with one angle that is bigger than a right angle?

● Can you both draw a hexagon with two angles that are bigger than a right angle?

● Can you both draw a hexagon with three angles that are bigger than a right angle?

● Can you both draw a hexagon with four angles that are bigger than a right angle?

● Can you both draw a hexagon with five angles that are bigger than a right angle?

Watch out! Some of these may be impossible!

● Bring all your drawings into school.

Dear Parent or Carer

We are working in class on different shapes and, also, on angles. Right angles are exactly 90°, acute angles are less than 90° and obtuse angles are more than 90°. There are many different hexagons – the most common are the rocket shape and the regular hexagon (which has equal sides and equal angles).

National Curriculum reference:
Maths Attainment Target
Shape, space and measures

_____and

child

_____

helper(s)

_____

did this activity together

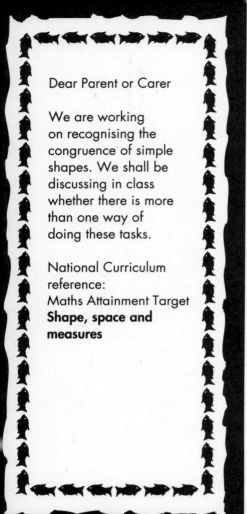
Smaller but the same!

● Look at the trapezium shown below.

Each of the small trapezium shapes are congruent! This means they are exactly the same shape and size.

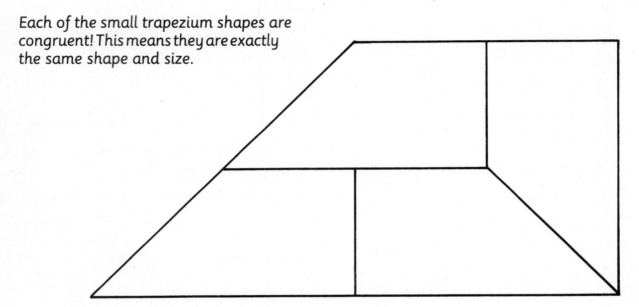

● Can you draw a square and divide it so that it contains four smaller, congruent squares?

● Can you draw a triangle and divide it so that it contains four smaller, congruent triangles?

● Bring all your drawings into school.

impact MATHS HOMEWORK

Reflections

Many patterns are produced by reflecting and repeating one simple shape. The example shown has been created by simply repeating the square in the bottom left-hand corner (not reflecting it, just sliding it along). This is called a 'translation'.

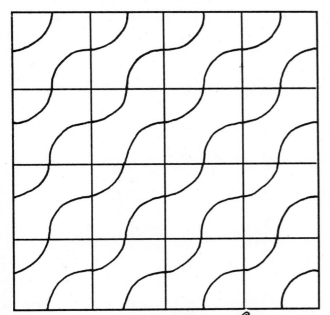

● Cut out the square in the bottom left-hand corner.

● Copy it as it is into the top left-hand corner of the blank grid below.

● For the next square along, REFLECT it by drawing its mirror image.

● Keep going like this to create a symmetrical pattern on the grid.

● Colour both grids and bring them into school.

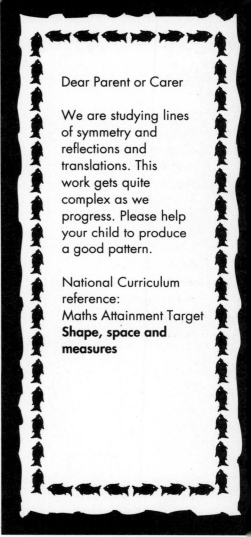

Dear Parent or Carer

We are studying lines of symmetry and reflections and translations. This work gets quite complex as we progress. Please help your child to produce a good pattern.

National Curriculum reference:
Maths Attainment Target
Shape, space and measures

_____and

child

_____

helper(s)

_____

did this activity together

Nesting pyramids

● Make a pyramid using the net provided below.

● Stick the net on to the back of an old Christmas or birthday card and cut it out.

● Fold it along the dotted lines and make a pyramid.

● Can you copy the net exactly, only smaller? Make a smaller pyramid which will fit inside the first one!

● Can you make an even smaller one as well?

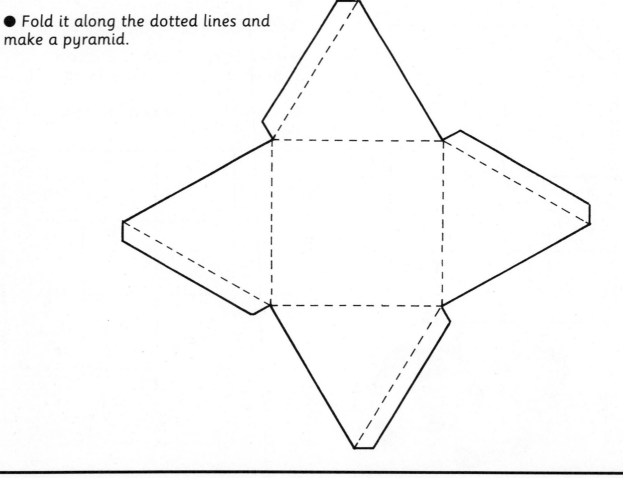

Acute, obtuse and reflex angles!

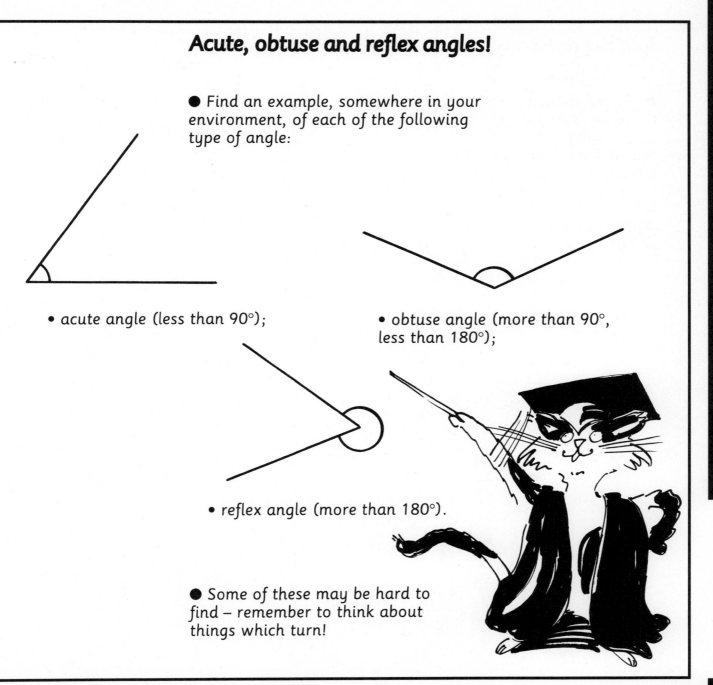

● Find an example, somewhere in your environment, of each of the following type of angle:

- acute angle (less than 90°);

- obtuse angle (more than 90°, less than 180°);

- reflex angle (more than 180°).

● Some of these may be hard to find – remember to think about things which turn!

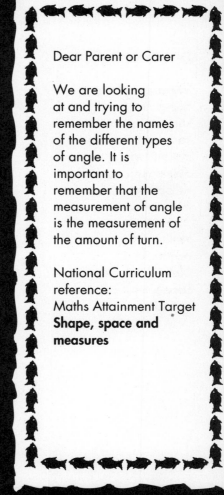

Dear Parent or Carer

We are looking at and trying to remember the names of the different types of angle. It is important to remember that the measurement of angle is the measurement of the amount of turn.

National Curriculum reference:
Maths Attainment Target
Shape, space and measures

_____and

child

_____

helper(s)

_____

did this activity together

Join the dots!

● Use the dotty circles below
to create some regular
and/or irregular shapes.
One has been done
for you.

● Which of your
shapes can you
name?

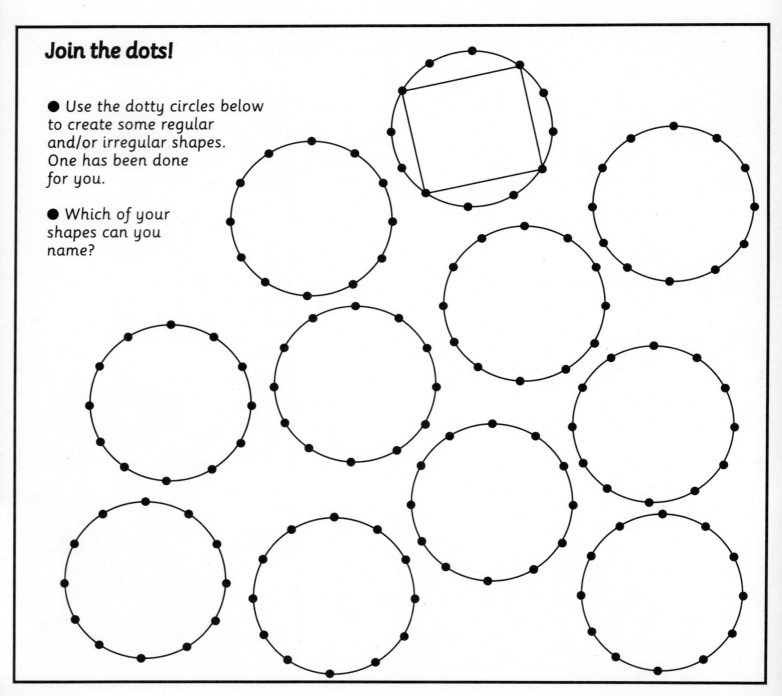

impact MATHS HOMEWORK

Envelopes

YOU WILL NEED: stiff paper, adhesive, a needle and thread.

● Cut out the diagram below and stick it on to a piece of stiff paper.

● Ask someone to help you to join all the dots to the crosses by stitching through the paper.

Make sure that you join a 1 to a 1 and a 2 to a 2 and so on.

● Bring your 'curve envelope' into school.

Dear Parent or Carer

The envelope of a curve is its shape created by a series of straight lines. If the lines are sufficiently close together this creates the illusion of a curve. This idea, that a curve can be envisaged as a series of very small straight lines, is the basis of calculus!

National Curriculum reference:
Maths Attainment Target
Shape, space and measures

_____and
child

_____
helper(s)

_____

did this activity together

_____and
child

_____
helper(s)

_____
did this activity together

Corner cut-offs!

- Cut out the 10cm × 20cm oblong at the bottom of the page.

- Cut out one square from each of the four corners.

- Fold up the sides to make a box.

- Calculate its volume.

- Now cut out corners of four squares each. Fold up the sides again.

- Calculate the volume of this box.

- Which box has the larger volume?

- Cut out larger corners. Fold up the sides to make a box and calculate its volume. Keep going like this for as long as seems sensible.

- Which box has the largest volume?

- Bring all your workings into school. ✂

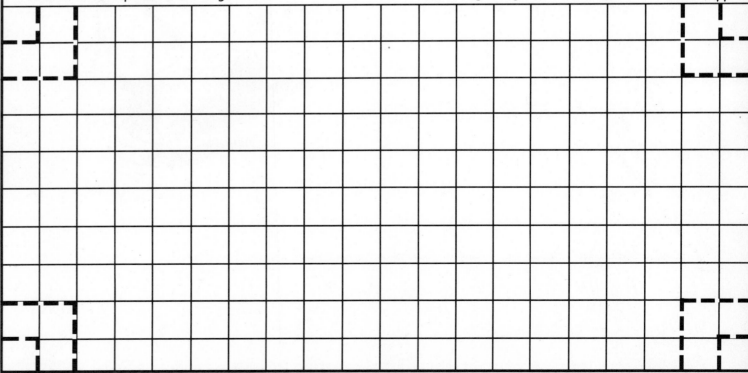

impact MATHS HOMEWORK

Icosahedrons!

This is a lovely shape to make!

● Stick the net below on to the back of an old Christmas or birthday card and cut it out. Score and then fold it along the dotted lines and make an icosahedron!

● Bring it into school.

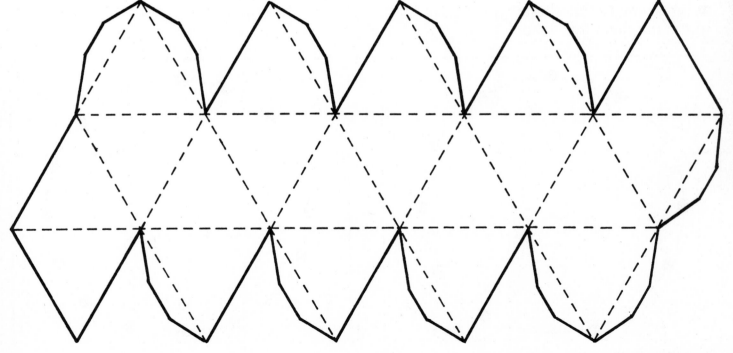

Dear Parent or Carer

We are exploring the ways in which two-dimensional shapes fold up to make three-dimensional shapes. This is one of our more complicated examples!

National Curriculum reference:
Maths Attainment Target
Shape, space and measures

_____and

child

_____

helper(s)

_____

did this activity together

_____and
child

_____
helper(s)

_____
did this activity together

Roses of mystery

● Choose one of the circles below and draw lines to join every dot to every other dot. Make sure you work methodically!

● Ask someone in your home to do the other one.

● Both of you colour them in.

● Whose 'rose' do you like best?

● Write your names beside your roses and bring them into school.

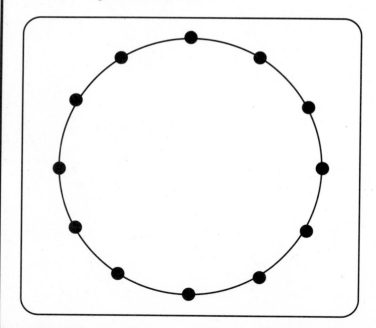

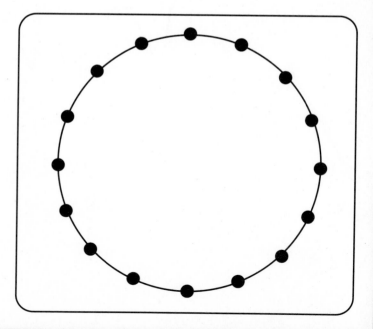

Ellipse

EACH OF YOU WILL NEED pens or pencils in two colours.

● Cut up this page so that you and your helper each have one of the two circles below to work on.

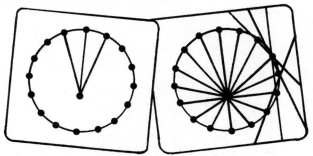

● Now both of you should try to make an ellipse. Use your first colour to join the dot marked F to each of the points round the circle.

● Use the other colour to draw a line at right angles to each of your rays at the point where they meet the circle. (See diagrams opposite!)

● This is hard! Bring your efforts into school.

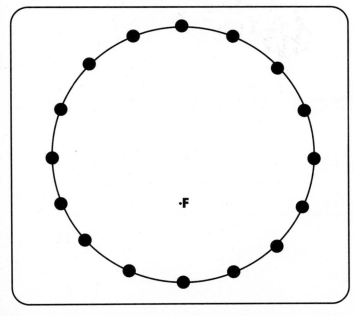

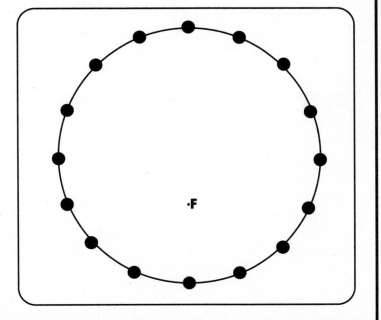

_____and

child

_____

helper(s)

_____

did this activity together

_____and
child

_____
helper(s)

_____
did this activity together

Kath's sandwiches

Kath is making sandwiches. She realises that she can make them by cutting the bread diagonally or straight.

She thinks about which is the best way to cut the sandwiches so that they can be eaten in the car! She wants each sandwich to have as much crust as possible per length of edge. (This stops the sandwich flopping!)

● Which way is she best to cut them?

● Perhaps you could try this activity with real sandwiches. Remember to ask first!

impact MATHS HOMEWORK

Three in a cube

● Stick the net below on to some thick paper or card. (The backs of old cards are excellent for this.) Cut it out and then use it as a template to make two more. Stick these nets on to card and cut them out also. Fold up the three nets and stick the tabs to make three slanted pyramids.

● What shape do they make when fitted together?

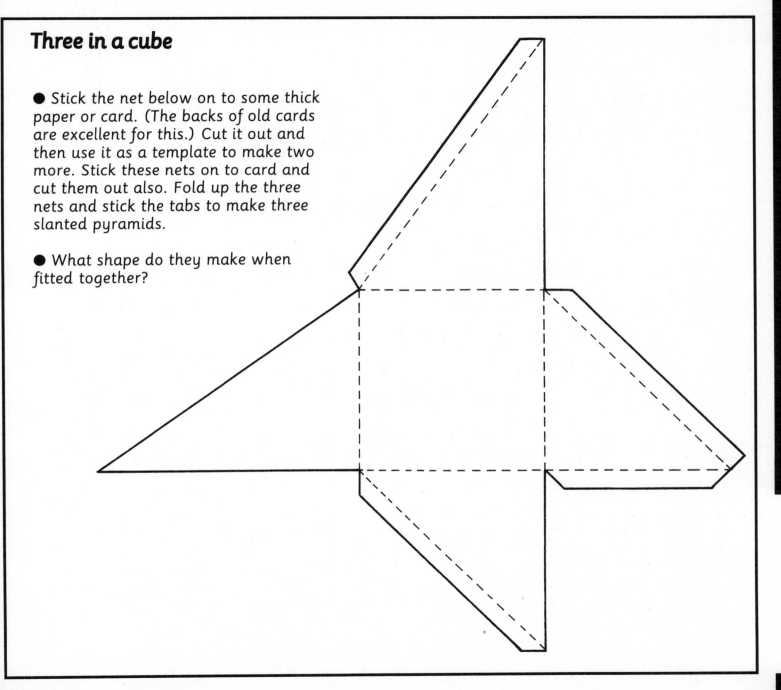

Dear Parent or Carer

We are dealing with the ways of making solid shapes from nets (that is, two-dimensional shapes). We shall be looking at different examples of nets in class.

National Curriculum reference:
Maths Attainment Target
Shape, space and measures

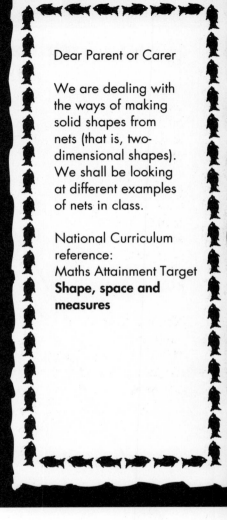

_____and

child

_____

helper(s)

_____

did this activity together

Nets 1 – tetrahedron and cube

Nets 2 – octahedron and dodecahedron

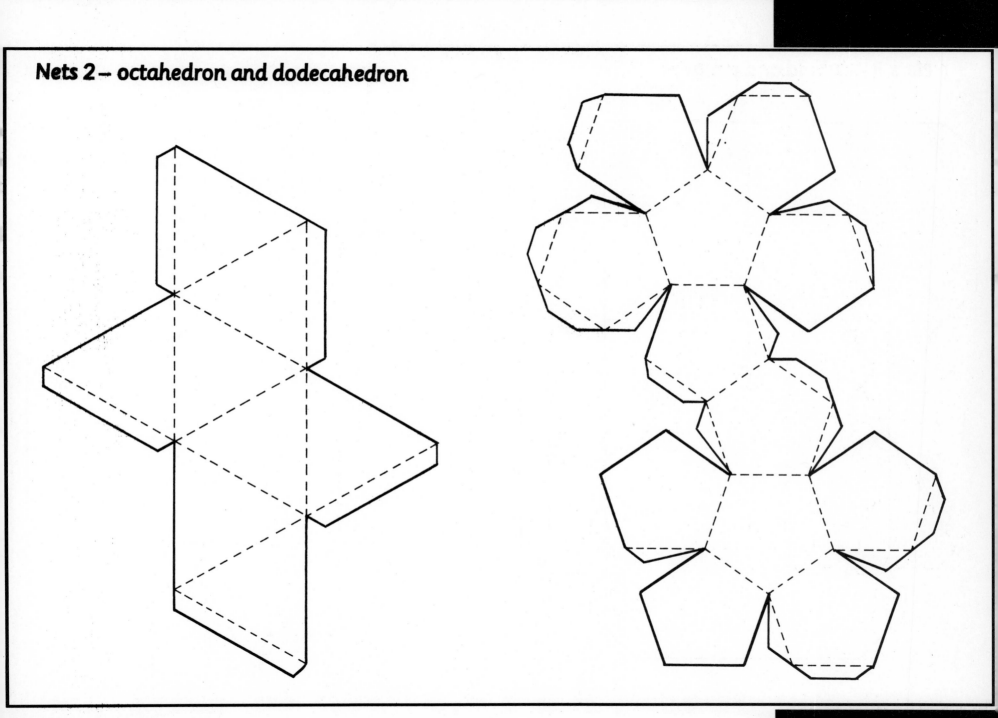

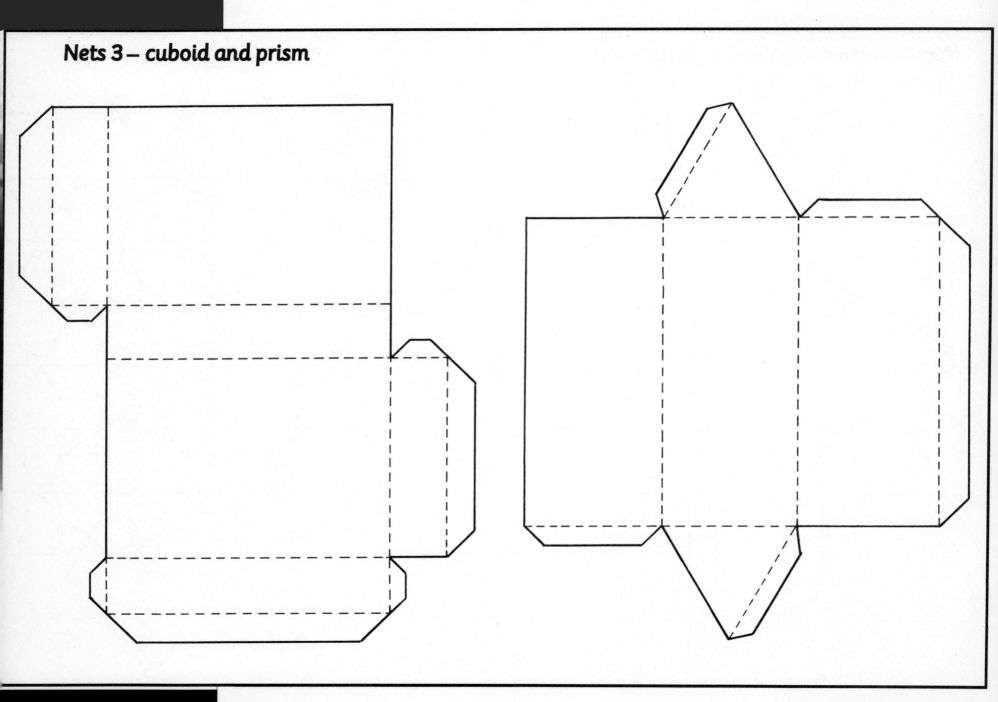

impact MATHS HOMEWORK

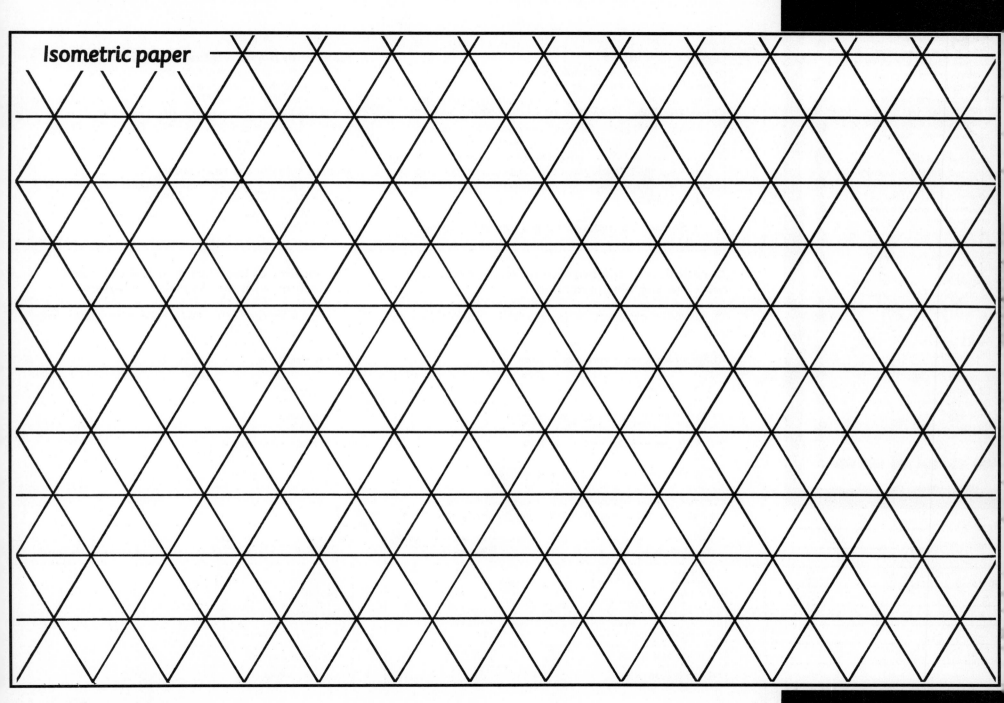

Isometric paper

IMPACT diaries

The IMPACT diaries provide a mechanism by means of which an efficient parent-teacher dialogue is established. Through these diaries, which last up to two years depending upon the frequency of the IMPACT tasks, teachers obtain valuable feedback both about children's performances on specific maths tasks and about the tasks themselves. Parents are able to alert the teacher to weaknesses and strengths and nothing about the child's performance in maths comes as a surprise at the end of the year or when statutory assessments are administered.

The diaries are a crucial part of this homework scheme.

Help with implementing IMPACT

Schools that wish to get IMPACT started by means of a series of staff meetings or in-service days may like to purchase the IMPACT INSET pack which contains everything that is needed for getting going. This is available from IMPACT Supplies Ltd, PO Box 1, Woodstock, Oxon OX20 1HB.

Useful telephone numbers

IMPACT Central Office (for information and assistance): 071 607 2789 at the University of North London on extension 6349. IMPACT Supplies Ltd (for diaries and INSET pack): 0993 812895.

Correlation of the Scottish maths curriculum with the English curriculum

The Scottish curriculum is divided into the Attainment Outcomes given below.

(PSE) Problem-solving and enquiry skills

(IH) Information handling

(NMM) Number, money and measurement

(SPM) Shape, position and movement

PSE is the equivalent of using and applying maths

IH permeates the Scottish maths curriculum, in that its requirements apply to all maths activities in NMM and SPM.

English subject	Scottish
Number	NMM
Money	NMM
Measuring	NMM
Number patterns	NMM
Shape and space	SPM
Data handling	IH

Correlation of the Northern Ireland maths curriculum with the English curriculum

The Northern Ireland curriculum is divided into the Attainment Targets (ATs) given below.

(AT N) Number

(AT A) Algebra

(AT M) Measures

(AT S) Shape and space

(AT D) Handling data

English subject	Northern Ireland
Number	AT N
Money	AT M
Measuring	AT M
Number patterns	AT A
Shape and space	AT S
Data handling	AT D